Editha B. Mills
535 Springdale
Athens, Georgia

THE SOUTHERN
FERN GUIDE

BOOKS BY EDGAR T. WHERRY

WILD FLOWERS OF MOUNT DESERT ISLAND, MAINE

GUIDE TO EASTERN FERNS

WILD FLOWER GUIDE

THE GENUS PHLOX

THE FERN GUIDE

THE SOUTHERN FERN GUIDE

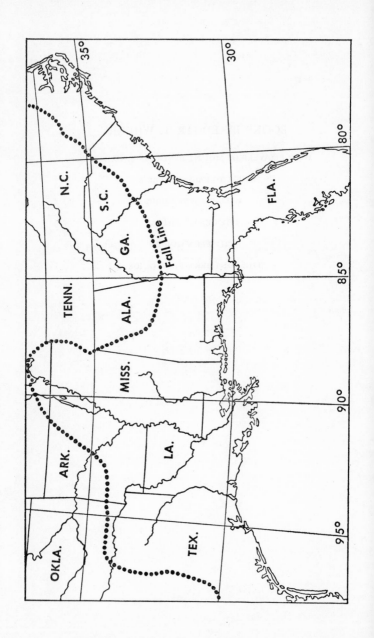

DOUBLEDAY NATURE GUIDES SERIES

THE SOUTHERN
FERN GUIDE

SOUTHEASTERN AND
SOUTH-MIDLAND UNITED STATES

BY

Edgar T. Wherry, Ph.D.

PROFESSOR OF BOTANY, EMERITUS
UNIVERSITY OF PENNSYLVANIA

ILLUSTRATED BY
James C. W. Chen, Ph.D.
AND
Keith C. Y. Chen

1964
DOUBLEDAY & COMPANY, INC.
Garden City, New York

DEDICATED TO THE MEMORY OF

JOHN KUNKEL SMALL,

EMINENT AUTHORITY ON THE

PLANTS OF THE SOUTHERN

STATES, WHO IN 1923

INTRODUCED ME TO OUR

SUBTROPICAL FERNS

CONTENTS

INTRODUCTION

The Fern Guide, published by Doubleday & Company in April 1961, dealt with some 135 species growing in eastern North America north of latitude 37°. This will also serve for identification of most ferns of the uplands of the southern states. In the lowlands of the latter, however, nearly 100 additional kinds grow, and come to the attention of both residents and visitors, so a similar *Guide* to these has been prepared. Illustrations of them have been drawn by James C. W. Chen and his brother Keith C. Y. Chen, Formosan students at the University of Pennsylvania and Ohio State University, respectively.

In organizing the material, use has of course been made of the latest work covering the region, *Ferns of the Southeastern States,* by John K. Small, 1938. Since that date, however, there have been many changes in nomenclature as well as new discoveries. Several books and many articles, which have appeared subsequently in periodical literature, have accordingly been consulted, and pertinent changes made.

An important source of information on new developments has been the *American Fern Journal,* a quarterly publication of the American Fern Society, Inc. Everyone who becomes interested in any phase of fern study will find it worth while to join this organization. Besides issuing the *Journal,* it sponsors meetings and field trips in various parts of the country, enabling members to become personally acquainted with one another. It maintains a spore exchange, through which those who wish to engage in the fascinating hobby of raising ferns from spores can obtain species from beyond their own regions. There is also a library and a herbarium, from which members may borrow books or specimens for study. Officers change frequently, but the address of a current secretary can be ascertained by inquiry at the botany department of any educational institution.

GLOSSARY OF TECHNICAL TERMS

acuminate: tapering to a point.

acute: ending in a point without tapering.

annulus: a ring of thick-walled cells on a sporangium.

apiculate: ending abruptly in a point of blade-tissue.

appressed: bent up against a stalk or margin.

areole: the space between veins which separate and rejoin.

auricle: an ear-like basal lobe or segment.

axis: an elongate stalk on which structures are borne.

basionym: the earliest name-combination including an epithet.

blade: the broad flat portion of a frond, leaf, or division.

capsule: a dry container of spores.

cilia: hairs extending from a margin.

circumneutral: from slightly acid to slightly alkaline.

combination: a genus name plus a species epithet.

compound: made up of multiple parts.

cone: an ellipsoid to cylindric group of sporophyls.

cordate: having two large basal lobes, with broad notch.

crenate: shallowly cut into rounded teeth.

deciduous: withering at the close of a growing season.

decurrent: tapering down along an axis.

digitate: in finger-like arrangement.

dimorphic: having dissimilar fertile and sterile blades.

disjunct: occurring at widely separated points.

elliptic: rounded in outline and longer than broad.

endemic: ranging over a limited area.

entire: having the margin uninterrupted by notches.

epithet: the technical name of a species or lower taxon.

exserted: extending beyond a margin or enclosing structure.

falcate: obliquely curved like a scythe-blade.

fertile: bearing reproductive organs, especially spores.

form (*forma;* abbrev., f.) : a minor variant of a species.

free: descriptive of veins which are separated at tip.

frond: the "leaf" of a fern, comprising stipe and blade.

gametophyte: the sexual stage in a life-cycle.
genus (pl., **genera**) : a group of closely related species.
glabrous: smooth; lacking hairs or scales.
gland: a waxy globule, often tipping a hair.

hybrid: the product of the union of sex cells of two species.

incised: cut in a coarse, irregular manner.
indusium: a thin sheet of pale tissue covering a fern sorus.
inferior: lying beneath or on the lower side of a structure.
internode: the portion of an axis between two nodes.

lanceolate: narrowed abruptly below and gradually to tip.
lateral: lying at the side of a structure.
linear: long and narrow with essentially parallel sides.
lobe: a short, rounded division of a blade.
lycosphen: a term to replace the inapt "fern-ally."

meadow: an open, moist, often grassy area.
medial: occupying a middle position.
megaspore: a relatively large female spore.
membranous: thinner in texture than ordinary blade-tissue.
microspore: a relatively small male spore.
midrib: a heavy vein medial in a blade or division.

node: the point on an axis at which structures arise.

oblong: parallel-sided and moderately longer than broad.
obsolete: disused or lacking.
obtuse: blunt or rounded-off at tip.
ovate: narrow-based, markedly widened, then short-tapering.
ovoid: egg-shaped; solid with ovate long-section.

palmate: divided into several diverging segments.
pedate: divided into segments decreasing outward like toes.
peltate: supported on a central stalk, as in an umbrella.
petiole: the stalk of a leaf; in ferns often termed a stipe.
phylum (pl., **phyla**) : a major division of the plant kingdom.
pinna: a primary blade-division, spaced along an axis.
pinnate: with spaced divisions in two rows along an axis.
pinnule: a primary pinna-division, similarly spaced.
pinnulet: a corresponding pinnule-division.

prothallium: the small plant constituting the gametophyte.
pubescent: bearing a hairy covering.

rachis: the axis of a pinnate blade, bare between pinnae.
reflexed: bent far backward or downward.
reniform: kidney-shaped; elliptic with a lateral notch.
reticulate: forming a network.
revolute: turned under at a margin.
rhizophore: a stalk interposed between stem and roots.
rootstock: an underground stem; may be erect or creeping.

scarious: thin, dry, lacking green color.
serrate: cut, like a saw, into acute forward-pointing teeth.
sessile: lacking a supporting stalk.
sheath: a sheet of tissue curved around a structure.
simple: undivided; all in one piece.
sinus: the notch or gap between lobes or segments.
sorus (pl., sori) : a patch of sporangium-bearing tissue.
species (*both* sing. and pl.) : the taxon subordinate to genus.
spike: an elongate compact group of reproductive structures.
sporangium (pl., sporangia) : a container of spores.
spore: a minute thick-walled reproductive cell.
sporocarp: a thick-walled pod-like spore-container.
sporophyl: a blade or leaf supporting sporangia.
sporophyte: the spore-bearing stage in a life-cycle.
stellate: radiating in star-like fashion.
sterile: not producing spores; opposed to fertile.
stipe: the stalk supporting the blade in a fern frond.
strand: a rope-like group of vascular cells.
subspecies: the major subdivision of a species.
superior: lying above or on the upper side of a structure.
swamp: a wet area grown up with trees or large shrubs.

taxon (pl., taxa) : a group of plants that can be classified.
ternate: spreading into three equal or subequal divisions.
truncate: ending abruptly straight across.
type: the original representative of a taxon.

variety (*varietas;* abbrev. v. or var.) : a species subdivision.
vascular: traversed by elongate tubular cells.

whorl: a radiating group of structures borne at a node.

ABBREVIATIONS

adj.: adjacent
Ala.: Alabama
alt.: altitude
Amer.: America
Ark.: Arkansas
bas.: basionym
c., centr.: central
ca.: (*circa*): about
Can.: Canada
cm.: centimeter
Co.: County
cult'd.: cultivated
diam.: diameter
e.: east, eastern
eastw.: eastward
Eu.: Europe
Euras.: Eurasia
f.: (*forma*): form
Fla.: Florida
Ga.: Georgia
L.: Lake
La.: Louisiana
lat.: latitude
long.: longitude
lowl.: lowland(s)
m.: meter
Mex.: Mexico
Miss.: Mississippi
mm.: millimeter
mts.: mountains
n.: north, northern

N.A., N. Amer.:
   North America
N.C.: North Carolina
no.: number
northw.: northward
Okla.: Oklahoma
Par.: Parish (in La.)
pen.: peninsula, peninsular
pl.: plural
pt.: point
R.: River
resp.: respective
s.: south, southern
S.A.: South America
S.C.: South Carolina
southw.: southward
sp.: species
ssp.: subspecies
sub-: under, less than
t.: taxon
Tenn.: Tennessee
Tex.: Texas
trop.: tropical
upl.: upland(s)
U.S.: United States
v., var.: variety
Va.: Virginia
vy.: valley
w.: west, western
W.I.: West Indies
westw.: westward

PRONUNCIATION OF TECHNICAL NAMES: In general *ch* is pronounced like *k*, as is also *c*, except when this precedes a "soft" vowel, when it is like *s*. Similarly, *g* is like *j* before soft vowels. In Greek diphthongs, *C* and *P* are silent with *T*. Over vowels, the grave accent ' signifies the long, the acute ' the short English sound.

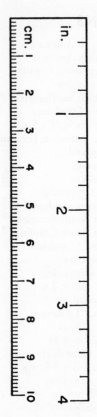

Measurements of plant parts are herein given in the metric system, of larger objects in centimeters (cm.) and of smaller in the 1/10-as-long millimeters (mm.). Since one cm. equals roughly 2/5 inch, multiplying a given number of cm. by 4 and then dividing by 10 will yield the equivalent in inches; for example, 5 cm. × 4 = 20, ÷ 10 = 2 in. Correspondingly, dividing a larger number of cm. by 30 will result in the approximate number of feet.

In the course of the field trips in the southern states on which data for this *Guide* have been obtained, the writer has received greatly appreciated aid from associates and local naturalists, of whom the following merit special mention: In long past years, Dr. John K. Small and Edward and Robert St. John; and more recently, John Beckner, James E. Benedict, Jr., Dr. Donovan S. Correll, Thomas Darling, Jr., C. Eugene Delchamps, Oliver M. Freeman, Ray and Ralph Garrett, and Edward M. Shields.

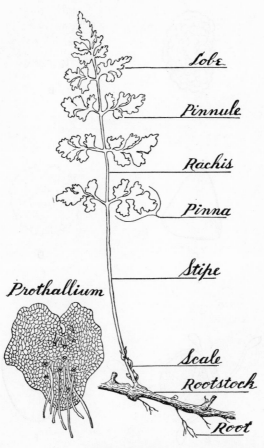

Lobe

Pinnule

Rachis

Pinna

Stipe

Prothallium

Scale

Rootstock

Root

FERN PLANTS

Left, Gametophyte, underside, enlarged. *Right,* Sporophyte.

Drawn by Peter D. Domville

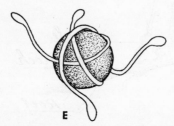

SPORES OF FERNS AND LYCOSPHENS

A. *Polypodium*
C. *Adiantum*
E. *Equisetum*

B. *Cystopteris*
D. *Osmunda*
F. *Lycopodium*

FERN LIFE CYCLE

The plant which we generally designate as a fern or a lycosphen constitutes the sporophyte stage in the life cycle—so-called, from the Greek for spore and plant, in that it produces the reproductive structures known as spores. These are minute one-celled objects, often developed in enormous numbers, which "fly through the air with the greatest of ease"—some even reaching the stratosphere. Sooner or later they fall to the earth's surface, and those which land in favorable spots proceed to germinate. The result is a bit of tissue a few mm. or rarely cm. in diameter, known as a prothallium. This represents the gametophyte stage in the cycle, that is, the plant which produces the sexual cells, or gametes.

In typical ferns, as shown in the illustration on page 17, the prothallium is a heart-shape flake. On the underside of this near the notch there develop cylindric structures known as archegonia, each of which contains an egg or female reproductive cell. Toward the opposite end, in the midst of thread-like appendages which serve as a sort of root, appear globose objects termed antheridia, from which emerge male sperms. These are propelled by cilia attached at one end, and swim through water films. They are attracted by secretions from an archegonium, and one enters its canal and fertilizes the enclosed egg. The result of this process, known as the zygote, then proceeds to grow into a new sporophyte, completing the cycle.

The shapes and surface sculptures of fern spores are often characteristic of genera or even species, meriting observation under a microscope. A small assemblage of them is placed on a slide, immersed in a drop of mounting medium—the so-called Permount being especially satisfactory—and a cover slip applied. In the more specialized groups they have one ridge and are termed monolete or bean-shaped. In primitive ones they are three-ridged or trilete; this is also the case in the Clubmosses and their relatives, the sculpture of which is best seen if mounted dry.

FERN CYTOLOGY

The general relations of chromosomes and their ploidy were discussed in some detail on pages 23 to 25 of *The Fern Guide*.* By now the chromosome numbers characterizing many fern genera have been ascertained, and it has been found that related ones have the same or but slightly different values. On the other hand, some which have been assumed on the basis of superficial features to lie close together prove to differ so widely in this respect that reconsideration of their systematic position is called for.

Basal Chromosome Numbers of Southern Lowland Genera

Acrostichum	30	Meniscium	36
Adiantum	29–30	Nephrolepis	41
Anemia	38	Notholaena	27
Asplenium	36	Onoclea	37
Athyrium	40	Ophioglossum	126
Blechnum	28–34	Osmunda	22
Botrychium	45–46	Pellaea	29–30
Campyloneurum	37	Phegopteris	30
Cheilanthes	29–30	Pityrogramma	30
Ctenitis	41	Polypodium	37
Cyclosorus	36	Polystichum	41
Cyrtomium	41	Pteridium	52
Cystopteris	42	Pteris	29
Dennstaedtia	32–34	Sphenomeris	39
Dicranopteris	39	Stenochlaena	37
Diplazium	41	Tectaria	40
Dryopteris	41	Thelypteris	27–36
Goniopteris	36	Trichomanes	18–34
Hymenophyllum	13	Trismeria	30
Hypolepis	52	Vittaria	30
Leptogramma	36	Woodsia	41
Lorinseria	35	Woodwardia	34–36
Lygodium	29–30		

* In condensing the text-matter to fit into p. 25 a word got left out twice from the second sentence, rendering it misleading; it should have read: "A tetraploid parent's sperm may fuse with a diploid parent's egg. . . ."

CLASSIFICATION

The plants treated herein are divided on the basis of morphology and anatomy into four PHYLA: (1) *Pteropsida,* (2) *Sphenopsida,* (3) *Lycopsida,* and (4) *Psilopsida.* The first, the most specialized, comprises both the flowering plants and the ferns, but only the latter are here considered. No. 2 represents the Horsetails and Scouring-rushes, No. 3 the Quillworts, Spike-mosses, and Clubmosses. Phylum 4 consists chiefly of extinct plants known only as fossils, but one of its few living members, the so-called Whisk Plant, grows in our region. For convenience the series as a whole is termed the *Pteridophytes.* Nos. 2, 3, and 4 often get classed as the "Fern-allies"; since this term is quite erroneous, a substitute, *Lycosphen,* made up of syllables from the names of Phyla 2 and 3, has been proposed, although a better one is needed.

FAMILIES: Among the *Lycosphens* no family uncertainties occur. In the fern division of the *Pteropsida* there are seven small families, with well-marked differentiating features, and containing in our region only from one to twenty taxa; in these no consequential problems of classification arise. Quite different is the situation, however, in the group comprising the vast majority of taxa, which is manifestly the most advanced, and is accordingly herein treated first. This was validly named Family *Polypodiaceae* by Ascherson in 1864; but in recent years there has been a tendency to divide it into multiple lesser families.

The chief proponents of this viewpoint have been Ching (1940), Holttum (1947), Copeland (1947), Alston (1956), and Pichi-Sermolli (1958). They differ so widely from one another, however, that it is deemed unrealistic to follow any one of them alone. Accordingly, the Family *Polypodiaceae* is being retained in its time-honored sense. Its component taxa are, however, grouped in accordance with notable features, and in the keys there are added the quasi-family names taken from one or another of the above-listed workers which correspond more or less closely to each group.

GENERA: One might suppose that during the 200-odd years since Linnaeus established the genus concept, the long series of earnest workers would have attained agreement as to fern genera; but alas, such is not the case. There are today marked differences of opinion among leading specialists, which have had to be considered in preparing this *Guide;* choices have been made on the basis of the best information available.

As an illustration, the situation in the *Polypodium* Group, comprising the first seven genera here accepted, may be discussed. The names adopted for these are (1) *Polypodium,* (2) *Campyloneurum,* (3) *Microgramma,* (4) *Goniophlebium,* (5) *Phymatodes,* (6) *Phlebodium,* and (7) *Paltonium.* Of these, five were named in the genus *Polypodium* by Linnaeus in 1753.

Some workers favor going back to Linnaeus, and classing the members of minor genera 2 to 6 as species of *Polypodium.* This would of course be the easy way, in that then no systematic and nomenclatorial complexities would have to be looked into or decisions made. But science would never advance if everyone followed the route of least resistance; moreover, that procedure would ignore the endeavors of the numerous workers who by close study have detected characters which may well be of significance. In the present *Guide* generic segregates are accepted in so far as they are manifestly based on sound observations and are recognized by competent authorities.

Questions as to the names which should be used for at least two of the above segregate genera then require consideration. The nomenclature of 3 is indeed in near-chaos; it has been shifted around to at least seven different genera, to say nothing of being assigned about as many species epithets. After thorough review, Copeland pointed out in 1947 that the earliest of these into which it can be made to fit by a minor expansion of the original definition is *Microgramma,* published by Presl in 1836, so this is adopted herein, and the necessary new name-combination made.

The other member of the *Polypodium* group as to which there is nomenclatorial difficulty is 5. In this case the combination *Polypodium phymatodes* was used by Linnaeus in 1753, his species epithet being raised to genus rank by Presl in 1836. A related genus had been named *Microsorium* by Link in 1833, and Copeland held that the two should be combined, in which case this earlier name would have to be used. On the other hand, both Christensen and Holttum maintained the distinctness of these genera, and their viewpoint is favored here, *Phymatodes* being accordingly adopted as the genus name. Problems of these sorts have arisen again and again in the compilation of this *Guide*.

For many years the morphology of sori and indusia have been much used as a basis for deciding relationships, but recent studies of anatomy and cytology have indicated that seemingly similar soral characters may have resulted from parallel evolution, and are not of phyletic significance at all.

That the linear outline of the sori of *Asplenium* and *Athyrium* does not indicate close relationship came to be realized on anatomical grounds in the 1940s. The vascular features of the stipe are especially significant; to study them, this may be cut with a sharp blade toward both base and top, and the surfaces observed under magnification. The strand-sections of the two are markedly unlike; and their distinctness was confirmed by cytologic study in 1950, the chromosome numbers proving to be discordant.

The resemblance of the reniform indusia of *Dryopteris* and *Thelypteris* led to their being united for nearly two centuries, and even today some fern students decline to separate them. Their distinctness is now generally accepted, however, since both their vascular strand pattern and chromosome numbers are markedly unlike. The dissimilar stipe anatomy of *Pteris* and *Pteridium* was long ignored, and they are kept together in "Family *Pteridaceae*" by Copeland and his disciples. Their now realized extreme difference in chromosome number confirms the other evidence that they do not belong in the same group.

SPECIES: The plan adopted in *The Fern Guide* for listing epithets is again being followed. Under the heading NOMEN-CLATURE the one accepted for each taxon is given in bold-face italics, with its basionym, or earlier use in another combination, if any. Choice of epithets is based on the fundamental principle of priority: the earliest published, starting with Linnaeus, 1753, accompanied by an adequate definition, is to be used. The writer favors accepting the original spelling of epithets (except compositors' errors or authors' oversights), not feeling competent to correct the Latin of earlier workers, as some present-day fern students do. Synonyms widely used in current literature are added, to aid anyone more familiar with them in finding the equivalent accepted herein.

SPECIES SUBDIVISIONS: While the primary subdivision of a species is currently termed a subspecies, few ferns have been named in this category, so it is being used only to a minor extent. On the other hand, variety (abbreviated var. or v.) is adopted for taxa deemed too closely related to be maintained as distinct species, yet exhibiting significant geographic differences. Being a part of a species, a variety can not be logically contrasted with the whole, but only with the type variety. The latter is currently often named by repeating the species epithet, but that leads to confusing double-talk and is not practiced herein. The still lower category form, abbreviated to f., is applied to sports which appear among normal plants and do not have any spatial separation or range.

HYBRIDS: Modern studies are showing that hybrids are not infrequent among ferns, and failure to recognize this has at times led to considerable confusion. They are designated by placing the symbol × between their parental names—customarily in alphabetical order—or before such presumed species epithets they may have received. In some cases their parents are manifestly well-known taxa, in others one or even both may be unrecognizable. Their spores are usually aborted and shrunken, but relatively large unreduced mother cells capable of germination may also be present in their sporangia.

SOUTHERN FERN DISTRIBUTION

On the map inserted as the frontispiece of this *Guide* there is drawn in addition to state boundaries a dotted line extending from northeast to southwest, with a bulge to the north in the midland states. This is known as the Fall Line, in reference to the occurrence of waterfalls in many streams near it. Several major cities are located along this line, since it marks the head of tide, which vessels could reach from the ocean when they were founded. It represents the position of the seashore at the beginning of Cretaceous geologic time about 125 million years ago.

North of this line lie the "southern uplands," underlain by rocks such as granite, sandstone, and limestone. From the standpoint of plant distribution, these uplands can be divided roughly into three provinces: The Piedmont Plateau, extending from the Fall Line to the mountain front, North Carolina to Alabama; the lower mountains, between altitudes of *ca.* 750 to 1500 feet, in these states and northern Arkansas; and the higher mountains, attaining heights of over 6000 feet in North Carolina and Tennessee. Many of the ferns which grow in these uplands are identical with those of northeastern North America, treated in *The Fern Guide;* they are briefly discussed and illustrated in the Appendix of the present work.

South of the Fall Line lie the "southern lowlands"; the geological formations here are largely unconsolidated sands and clays, although there are local outcrops of limestone and sandstone. Altitudes are low and the climate is accordingly relatively mild. Here many ferns are identical with or related to those of the countries to the south—the West Indies, Mexico, Central and even South America. Some sorts widespread in the north extend, however, well down into these lowlands, and their descriptions and illustrations as given in *The Fern Guide* are reprinted herein, with the appropriate changes in measurement and range data.

25

The fern habitats of the southern uplands are essentially the same as those in the northeastern states, but three more characteristic of the lowlands merit special discussion, namely "epiphytic habitat," "sink," and "hammock."

In the southern lowlands a number of ferns grow chiefly perched on trunks or branches of trees, and are termed epiphytes from the Greek for "upon a plant." They are not, as often supposed, parasites, drawing no nourishment from the sap of the tree, which may indeed be dead. The woody material into which their roots extend is relatively low in nutrients and acid in reaction, conditions to which they have become adapted. Should they fall to the ground, they are likely to die because the soil may be too rich or too low in acidity for their needs; they may persist, however, on the acid humus of rotting logs, stumps, etc.

When rain water falls on an outcrop of limestone, it gradually dissolves this away, and in the process may develop hollows which are known as sink-holes, or for short, sinks. (They occur in the uplands too, but are more frequent in lowland areas.) These vary in diameter and in depth from a few inches to hundreds of feet; they may be dry or partly filled with water. The soil in them is usually essentially neutral, and their moisture and temperature conditions are relatively constant. A considerable number of ferns thrive around their rims or down their walls as far as sufficient light can reach.

The Indian term *hammock* signifies a patch of broad-leaved trees in the midst of pineland or grassland, and is not the same as hummock, a diminutive of hump, an elevation. Hammocks may be developed on islands standing above the general level, but often occur in damp depressions and around sinks and springs. The similarity of the two words has led to so much confusion among laymen and scientists alike that it is here deemed wise to replace the term hammock by woodland, as a habitat to be contrasted with pineland.

Fern spores, being minute and light, are readily carried around by moving air. Most of them fall onto unfavorable places and come to naught, but over the years a few land in spots where they are able to germinate and start colonies. Species growing in the southern uplands, the ancestral home of which was farther north, have evidently been brought there by the strong winds which blow from that direction. To reach the southern lowlands from tropical America, spores can have readily been carried by hurricanes, which occur frequently.

In Small's *Ferns of the Southeastern States* (1938) frequent reference is made to two supposed invasions of Florida by tropical ferns. Species which grow toward the northern part of the peninsula are inferred to have arrived there during Oligocene geologic time some 15 million years ago, those toward the south end only during the past few thousand years, since the land there emerged from the sea. Geological evidence indicates, however, that much of the southern lowlands and *all* of Florida (except for a few isolated hills) were covered by the sea during interglacial periods. These were times when practically all the earth's surface ice melted, raising sea level 200 or 300 feet above its present position; and the last, known to geologists as the Sangamon, came to an end only around 75,000 years ago. Differences in area occupied by individual species are, then, to be ascribed to the routes of the hurricanes which brought in their spores in subsequent years.

Where spores happen to fall is of considerable importance. While some species seem rather indifferent to soil conditions, many show an apparent preference for certain levels of acidity, moisture, temperature, and so on. In the paragraph under each species herein treated headed HABITAT, the conclusions from field observations are stated. When the writer has been unable to study a given sort in its natural habitat, notes made by collectors have been utilized, and soil-acidity values ascertained by tests on soil scraped from the roots of herbarium specimens. For the many species which thrive best on limestone, the soil reaction ranges from slightly acid to slightly alkaline, and is accordingly termed "circumneutral."

In this *Guide* the RANGES of the species, so far as known up to 1960, are stated by portions of states or by counties. Lack of space renders the listing of exact localities impracticable, but these can be ascertained from the literature or herbarium labels. Some sorts are known to be extending their ranges and can be expected to turn up beyond the limits given. Others, alas, are becoming rarer or even extinct as man expands his activities ever farther into previously undisturbed areas.

In the chapter headed "Exploring for Ferns" in *The Fern Guide,* the need for more field work was pointed out. Even in northeastern North America, where naturalists have been active for three centuries, ranges of native ferns are still being extended and new taxa discovered from time to time. As far less exploration has been carried out in the region covered by the present *Guide,* there is much greater opportunity to advance our knowledge of the ferns.

What happened in northwestern peninsular Florida is an illustration of the possibilities. In 1932 Dr. Edward P. St. John, a northern teacher of classics, retired and picked out Floral City, in Citrus County, Florida, as a place to live. Having been an amateur fern student, he started looking for these plants, but at first could find none of interest in the nearby swamps, woods, and pinelands. Then his attention was called to the existence of limestone outcrops, grottoes, and sinks not far away, and he began to encounter sorts new to his experience. He invited his brother Robert P. St. John, whose interests were similar, to join him, and they proceeded to explore the three contiguous counties intensively.

In a few years they had found several species new to science, many previously known only in remote tropical America, and still more supposed to be limited to distant parts of Florida. When one considers the number of essentially unexplored areas not only in Florida but in all the states of our region, it is manifest that many more fern finds remain to be made.

Anyone who carries out systematic search for ferns can not fail to be impressed by the fundamental importance of rock or soil characters. Wherever in our region there is a considerable outcrop of sandstone or limestone undisturbed by man, notable finds can be expected. The success of the St. John brothers in areas of the latter rock has already been pointed out; they made some discoveries in sandy barrens as well.

Once there was an isolated hill of limestone in sandy country in Winn Parish, Louisiana, the ferns of which were fortunately collected in 1912 before man quarried it away. Two species found were upland ones not otherwise known in that lowland state. In contrast, a sandstone ridge in Natchitoches Parish has proved to support a disjunct lowland occurrence of the subacid-soil Hairy Lip Fern.

The St. John brothers one day found the Plateau Bristle Fern, a tiny moss-like plant, in a limestone sink. This was unexpected, in that its soils at upland stations had been found to be acid; so the writer arranged a visit. The remarkable feature of the occurrence was that there were many limestone rocks lying around, several supporting a Bristle Fern known elsewhere in the neighborhood; but the new find was limited to a single slab. This proved to consist of chert, a form of silica, the soil on which was correspondingly somewhat acid. The spores may have been blown by a tornado from the Alabama uplands, or by a hurricane from the mountains of Santo Domingo, the nearest known occurrences of the species in the respective directions. After being carried at random over hundreds of miles, one chanced to fall on a single rock a few feet across where the soil met its needs!

Climate, of course, has a bearing on fern distribution too, some tropical species being unable to withstand winter's cold anywhere north of the tip of the Florida peninsula, while others of northern range find the peninsula too hot in summer. Both sorts can mingle in sinks, however, since the temperature there changes little the year round.

FERN CULTURE

Naturalistic fern gardening, as practiced in the north and the southern uplands, becomes less frequent southward, and in peninsular Florida is carried on only by a few specialists. This is due to the relatively unfavorable environmental conditions involving climate, soil, weeds, fungi, and animal pests. In wooded areas, to be sure, a few climbers, epiphytes, Sword Ferns, etc., may be used for their "tropical effect"; but otherwise ferns are grown restricted to soil pockets in patios, pots, hanging baskets, etc. Dealers offer various exotics, such as the Brakes, Davallias, Staghorn Ferns, and so on; but special attention will be given here to the numerous native sorts deserving of cultural use. Much information along this line has been kindly furnished by Mr. John Beckner, a botanist and horticulturist of Sarasota, Florida, who has had practical experience in growing nearly every fern native to our region.

To produce media for fern culture, the following are currently used:

MINERAL MATERIALS: River gravel—$\frac{1}{4}$- to $\frac{1}{2}$-inch silica pebbles. Sand, inland—clean white coarse grains (beach sand is too salty for safe use). Turkey grit—fine granite chips. Agritex, perlite, vermiculite, etc., which represent expanded lava or mica (avoid plasterer's grade).

HUMUS MATERIALS: Peat, imported sorts, well broken up. Sphagnum moss, collected from a bog, dried, and sieved. Fir bark, as sold commercially in bags. Osmunda peat, black (the brown grades may prove unsatisfactory). Tree-fern fiber, imported from Mexico.

For ferns in general, the four mineral and two or three of the humus materials are mixed in roughly equal volumes. For epiphytes, the gravel and sand are preferably replaced by additional portions of sphagnum and fiber.

FERTILIZERS: For quick results, a commercial blue-tinted soluble grade, with the high-nitrogen formula 30–10–10 is favored, although various other ratios are also satisfactory. Steamed bone meal is slow-acting, but long-lasting.

FUNGICIDES: The most widely used are Agrimycin (copper-free), Manzate, and Captan. Especially successful is a weekly application of 4 oz. Agrimycin and ½ oz. Manzate in a 3-gallon Hozeon, a dilution of about 1 to 15.

PESTICIDES: The best yet found for controlling scale and mealy-bugs is Tedion. Never use Malathion or Parathion, as they damage ferns. Slugit has proved successful against slugs and snails.

FERN BEDS: These should be preferably not over 3 ft. wide (or if accessible from both sides, 6 ft.), and may well extend a few inches above ground level so as not to be inundated during heavy rains. Erosion and weed growth can both be minimized by covering with a 1-inch layer of river gravel, or a sheet of black plastic held down at the edges. For sorts requiring especially moist conditions, a plastic sheet may also be placed under the bed. Plastic bags are useful, not only for transporting the roots of collected ferns, but also for inverting over these to prevent drying out until well established.

CONTAINERS: For many ferns the commercial plastic are satisfactory, the 4- or 6-inch-square sizes being most widely used. For massive species, however, 1-foot clay pots with several inches of river gravel in the bottom are to be recommended. The small plastic baskets widely sold are too flimsy, but welded wire ones are suitable. Best of all are those made by hollowing out sections of trunks of Mexican tree ferns. Sawed pieces of the latter are excellent for growing epiphytes; they are available commercially in slabs around 6 to 10 inches wide, and in "totems," or prisms, about 2 inches square and of assorted lengths. Packing live sphagnum around the roots often helps the epiphytes get started on the surface of the tree-fern wood. To hold the plants against the support, plastic-covered wire should be used.

Native ferns of cultural interest comprise:

AQUATICS. Floating Ferns (*Azolla, Salvinia*). Will rapidly cover any well-lighted water surface, from the smallest aquarium to the largest garden pool.

Water Ferns (*Ceratopteris*). May be rooted in mud just beneath the water surface or left to float free. Can also be anchored in sand or grit in the bottom of an aquarium. Grow best in partial shade.

Water-clover Ferns (*Marsilea*). Readily grown in pool or aquarium. While the blades are ornamental, they tend to become overabundant.

EPIPHYTES. Many of these do not require the high perches they occupy in nature, but will grow in pots or even beds. The soil mixture suggested above may suffice for them, but is preferably replaced by one higher in humus, as: Perlite and turkey grit, 1 part each; fir bark and sifted sphagnum, 2 parts each. They of course are most likely to thrive on supports, and especially in hanging baskets, if these are well lined with sphagnum or with Osmunda peat, to hold moisture.

Auricled Spleenwort (*Asplenium auritum*). Requires considerably more moisture than it seems to in nature.

New World Birds-nest Fern (*Asplenium serratum*). Needs deep shade and high humidity, as well as an ample container.

Narrow Strap Fern (*Campyloneurum angustifolium*). Attractive as a hanging-basket subject, but difficult to grow otherwise. On the other hand, the Tailed Strap Fern (*C. costatum*), also with arching fronds, does well on supports if kept moist and well shaded.

Long Strap Fern (*Campyloneurum phyllitidis*). Easy to grow in almost any situation. The related Broad Strap Fern (*C. latum*) is more cold-sensitive.

Clinging-vine Fern (*Microgramma heterophylla*). Needs deep shade, high humidity, and protection against cold. If started in a shallow pot of well-drained humus, will proceed to climb up a tree-fern totem.

Sword Ferns (*Nephrolepis*). All of these do about as well as epiphytes as in soil; they should be used with caution, since they spread with disconcerting rapidity.

Ribbon Fern (*Paltonium lanceolatum*). Can be grown on tree-fern supports under moist shady conditions.

Gold-foot Fern (*Phlebodium aureum*). An outstanding subject for cultivation; will grow in almost any of the soils and garden situations here discussed.

Comb and Plumy Rockcap Ferns (*Polypodium pectinatum* and *P. plumula*). Can be grown on tree-fern supports or in humus-rich soil mixtures, but need constant watering.

Resurrection Fern (*Polypodium polypodioides*). Often brought into gardens as mats stripped from the trees on which it grows naturally. It can then be fastened to any desired support, but should be kept well moistened until it has taken hold on the new surface.

Whisk Plant (*Psilotum nudum*). Can be transplanted into a soil mixture if care is taken not to injure the delicate rootstock. Best introduced, however, by sawing off a tree stump or cypress knee which it has colonized. May come up from spores in cultures of other plants.

Shoestring Fern (*Vittaria lineata*). Unexpectedly difficult to establish in culture. In contrast its Broad-scale relative (*V. filifolia*) grows well on supports, although very sensitive to cold.

TERRESTRIAL FERNS. Many of our species, even though their native habitats are diverse, can be grown in the soil mixes above formulated, placed in beds, pots, or even baskets, if kept shaded and well watered. One or more species of the following genera will also do well in sunny situations: *Anemia, Blechnum, Cheilanthes, Cyclosorus, Goniopteris, Hypolepis, Lorinseria, Lycopodium, Nephrolepis, Ophioglossum, Psilotum, Pteridium, Pteris, Selaginella, Sphenomeris, Thelypteris, Trismeria,* and *Woodwardia.*

WEEDY FERNS. Certain taxa spread so rapidly by rootstocks or stolons that they are best kept out of restricted cultural areas: *Blechnum serrulatum, Cyclosorus gongylodes, Hypolepis repens, Nephrolepis* species, *Ophioglossum petiolatum, Pteridium* species, *Thelypteris augescens* and *T. palustris, Woodwardia virginica.* Sporelings of these as well as of *Cyclosorus dentatus,* etc., may also have to be watched for and weeded out.

RAISING FERNS FROM SPORES

While many exotic and a few native ferns can be purchased from dealers, most of our own species must be obtained otherwise. Abundant sorts may be dug freely from their native haunts, but removing rare ones could lead to their extermination. Raising ferns in general from their spores is not only a contribution to conservation, but a rewarding experience. Articles on various procedures for spore culture have appeared from time to time in the pages of the *American Fern Journal* and elsewhere; individual experimenters may have to find out by trial and error which will succeed best under their conditions.

Spore culture can be carried out in flats, clay flower pots, glass or plastic dishes, and so on. These should be sterilized by heat, or in case of the last-named, by some household disinfectant. A thick layer of porous material such as vermiculite is best placed in the bottom. The culture medium is then put in, up to within 2 or 3 cm. of the rim. It is customarily made up of a mixture of sandy loam and humus, put through a sieve of 1- or 2-mm. mesh, and baked in an oven for an hour or so at 250° F. The whole is then soaked in pure water (city tap water is sometimes toxic to young ferns), and drained until the surface is damp though not manifestly wet or muddy.

Spores are scraped from dried, mature sori, sifted through fine-textured fabric to remove debris, and strewn thinly over the surface. A transparent lid or cover is then applied, and the whole exposed to day- (not sun-) light, preferably supplemented by fluorescent tubes turned on at dusk and off at dawn by a timer. The soil should be kept damp by a mist-producing sprayer. In a few weeks there will appear on the surface a green film, which will develop into prothallia, from which in due time the infant sporophytes will arise, the cover being then removed. When deemed large enough to handle, these are transplanted to increasingly larger containers, and finally to their permanent location.

SOUTHERN FERN FLORAS

Ferns of the Southeastern States. John K. Small, 1938. Published by the author; now out of print.

ALA.: "The Fern Flora of Alabama." E. W. Graves, 1920. *American Fern Journal,* Vol. 10.

ARK.: "Arkansas Pteridophyta." Dwight M. Moore, 1940. *American Fern Journal,* Vol. 30.

FLA.: *Ferns of Florida.* John K. Small, 1931. Published by the author; obtainable from book dealers.

FLA.: "A County Check-list of Florida Ferns and Fern Allies." Donovan S. Correll, 1938. *American Fern Journal,* Vol. 28.

GA.: *Ferns of Georgia.* Rogers McVaugh and Joseph H. Pyron, 1951. University of Georgia Press, Athens.

LA.: *Ferns and Fern Allies of Louisiana.* Clair A. Brown and Donovan S. Correll, 1942. Louisiana State University Press, Baton Rouge.

MISS.: List of Pteridophytes in *Plants of Mississippi.* E. N. Lowe, 1921. Mississippi State Geological Survey.

N.C.: *Ferns of North Carolina.* H. L. Blomquist, 1934. Duke University Press, Durham.

N.C.: "A County Check-list of North Carolina Ferns and Fern Allies." H. L. Blomquist and D. S. Correll, 1940. *Journal Elisha Mitchell Scientific Society,* Vol. 56.

S.C.: "The Ferns and Fern Allies of South Carolina." Velma D. Matthews, 1940–41. *American Fern Journal,* Vols. 30 and 31.

TENN.: *Ferns of Tennessee.* Jesse M. Shaver, 1954. Bureau of Publications, George Peabody College, Nashville.

TEX.: *Ferns and Fern Allies of Texas.* Donovan S. Correll, 1955. Southern Methodist University Press, Dallas. 2nd ed., 1956. Texas Research Foundation, Renner.

KEYS

A key is a device for aiding in the identification of taxa by contrasting their respective characters, like the clues followed by detectives. While those furnished in different works may vary in detailed arrangement, they are customarily presented in an abbreviated form, with only nouns and adjectives, or analogous subjects and modifiers, stated, the user being expected to supply verbs and other articles of speech.

Referring to the first two families keyed on the next page, an alternative arrangement would have certain lines inset instead of lettered, thus:

Sporangia borne in sori, strips, or sheets beneath blade.
    Capsule stalked; annulus vertical: **1. Common Fern Family**
    Capsule sessile; annulus horizontal: **2. Net Fern Family**
Sporangia borne otherwise. . . .

The lettered couplet plan is favored here, in that contrasted sets of characters always lie side by side, rather than more or less separated by inset lines, which may become inconveniently numerous.

In any case, the inserts here italicized are to be made:

B. *If the* sporangia *are* borne in sori, strips or sheets beneath *the* blade, *proceed to lines headed* C *and* C'.

B'. *If the* sporangia *are* borne otherwise, *to* D *and* D'.

C. *If* (*in the sporangium*) *the* capsule *is* stalked *and the* annulus *is* vertical, *the specimen at hand belongs to*
                            1. The Common Fern Family

C'. *If the* capsule *is* sessile *and the* annulus *is* horizontal, *the specimen belongs to* . . . . . **2. The Net Fern Family**

Successive keys are given below to families, in the "common fern family" to groups, to genera, and to species. As in *The Fern Guide,* taxa are taken up in order from those deemed most specialized to those manifestly most primitive.

Ferns : Key to Families

A. Habitat terrestrial, or if rooted under water, the fronds well emersed; spores of one kind: B, B'.

A'. Habitat aquatic or temporarily in mud; spores of two kinds, male and female: G, G'.

B. Sporangia borne in sori, strips, or sheets beneath blade: C, C'.

B'. Sporangia borne otherwise: D, D'.

C. Capsule stalked; annulus vertical: **1. Common Fern Family***

C'. Capsule sessile; annulus horizontal: **2. Net Fern Family**

D. Tissue 1 or 2 cells thick; sori borne on bristles; sporangia small; annulus oblique: . . . . **3. Filmy Fern Family**

D'. Tissue many cells thick; sori not developed; sporangia relatively large: E, E'.

E. Annulus terminal; sporangia borne in double rows beneath narrow blade-divisions: . . . **4. Climbing Fern Family**

E'. Annulus obscure or lacking; sporangia borne openly in clusters or rows: F, F'.

F. Frond comprising a stipe and a blade; sporangia in compound clusters: . . . . **5. Royal Fern Family**

F'. Frond comprising a stipe bearing a sterile blade and a fertile segment; sporangia in compound clusters or in a double row: . . . . **6. Adders-tongue Family**

G. Plants rooted in mud, the blade if any floating when water covers this: . . . . . . **7. Water-clover Family**

G'. Plants floating, tiny: . . . . **8. Floating Fern Family**

---

* This major family has been divided by several recent fern workers into multiple minor groups, treated as if they were families. Their viewpoints differ too widely, however, for any one to be acceptable. In this *Guide* the Common Fern Family is being divided into "groups," named for representative genera; then in the genus keys an equivalent technical name with the standard family ending *aceae* is added. In some cases, *e.g. Aspleniaceae, Vittariaceae,* there is general agreement as to the naturalness of these groups. In many, however, the groups recognized here differ in content from those accepted in other treatments. This matter is further discussed at the end of the key to the genera, page 42.

1. Common Fern Family : Key to Groups

A. Stipe-base jointed to rootstock; blade entire, lobed, or subpinnate; sori circular or rarely elongate; indusium lacking:
1. **Polypodium Group**

A'. Stipe-base not jointed to rootstock: B, B'.

B. Indusium under or behind round sorus: 2. **Woodsia Group**

B'. Indusium above or beside sorus or lacking: C, C'.

C. Discrete sori lying astride or along veins well in from margins: D, D'.

C'. Discrete sori tipping veins at or toward margins, or not
formed: H, H'.

D. Texture thinnish; strands 2, flattened, united upward; indusium delicate or lacking: E, E'.

D'. Texture thickish; strands various; indusium firm: F, F'.

E. Sorus-outline round (or rarely elongate, then lacking indusium): . . . . 3. **Thelypteris Group**

E'. Sorus-outline linear; indus. present: 4. **Athyrium Group**

F. Stipe-scales copious; sori round; strands multiple, free:
5. **Dryopteris Group**

F'. Stipe-scales sparse; sori elongate; strands 2, cylindric,
united upward: G, G'.

G. Sorus-bearing veins along midrib: . 6. **Blechnum Group**

G'. Sorus-bearing veins diverging: . . 7. **Asplenium Group**

H. Sporangia forming sheets: . . . 8. **Acrostichum Group**

H'. Sporangia forming sori or soral strips: I, I'.

I. Tissue succulent or lax; habit peculiar: J. J'.

I'. Tissue firm; habit normal: K, K'.

J. Plant aquatic, with a pad of sterile and a tuft of branched
fertile fronds: . . . . 9. **Ceratopteris Group**

J'. Plant epiphytic; fronds linear: . . . 10. **Vittaria Group**

K. Sori borne on inner surface of reflexed marginal flaps:
11. **Adiantum Group**

K'. Sori borne on underside or margin of blade: L, L'.

L. Veins ending in marginal soral strips: M, M'.

L'. Veins ending in discrete sori: N, N'.

M. Soral strip of confluent sori: . . 12. **Cheilanthes Group**

M'. Soral strip of sporangia borne on a heavy cross-vein:
14. **Pteridium Group**

N. Sorus-position infra-marginal: . 13. **Nephrolepis Group**

N'. Sorus-position marginal: . . . 15. **Dennstaedtia Group**

Common Fern Family : Keys to Genera

1. *Polypodium* Group : "Polypodiaceae," restricted.

A. Veins free; blade cut into segments: .   .   1. *Polypodium*
A'. Veins areolate: B, B'.
B. Blade simple: C, C'.
B'. Blade cut into segments: E, E'.
C. Sporangia in long submarginal strips: .   .   7. *Paltonium*
C'. Sporangia in circular or elliptic sori: D, D'.
D. Habit tufted; fronds large: .   .   .   .   2. *Campyloneurum*
D'. Habit climbing; fronds small: .   .   .   3. *Microgramma*
E. Segments narrowed at base, the blade thus subpinnate; sori in multiple inframedial rows: .   .   4. *Goniophlebium*
E'. Segments broad-based; sori in medial rows: F, F'.
F. Sori impressed, with bulges behind: .   .   5. *Phymatodes*
F'. Sori surficial, tipping paired veinlets: .   .   6. *Phlebodium*

2. *Woodsia* Group : "Woodsiaceae"

A. Fronds dimorphic; indusium persistent: .   .   1. *Onoclea*
A'. Fronds uniform; indusium short-lived: B, B'.
B. Indusium inferior, splitting into segments: .   2. *Woodsia*
B'. Indusium behind sorus, shriveling: .   .   .   3. *Cystopteris*

3. *Thelypteris* Group : "Thelypteridaceae"

A. Blade broad-triangular; indusium none: .   1. *Phegopteris*
A'. Blade narrow-triangular to narrow-based: B, B'.
B. Sorus elongate; indusium none: .   .   .   2. *Leptogramma*
B'. Sorus round: C, C'.
C. Veins all (or nearly all) free: .   .   .   .   6. *Thelypteris*
C'. Veins in part united to a 3-rayed star: D, D'.
D. Vein-union occurring nearly throughout: .   3. *Meniscium*
D'. Vein-union occurring only toward midrib: E, E'.
E. Hairs in part branched: .   .   .   .   .   .   4. *Goniopteris*
E'. Hairs all simple: .   .   .   .   5. *Cyclosorus*

4. *Athyrium* Group : "Athyriaceae"

A. Sori in part paired: .   .   .   .   1. *Diplazium*
A'. Sori all single: .   .   .   .   2. *Athyrium*

5. Dryopteris Group : "Aspidiaceae"

A.   Rootstock climbing; indusium pseudopeltate: **1. Maxonia**
A'. Rootstock not climbing: B, B'.
B.   Veins areolate: C, C'.
B'. Veins free: D, D'.
C.   Tissue little thickened; indusium various: . **2. Tectaria**
C'. Tissue much thickened; indusium peltate: **3. Cyrtomium**
D.   Indusium peltate: . . . .   **4. Polystichum**
D'. Indusium reniform: E, E'.
E.   Minor axes not decurrent; hairs jointed: . . **5. Ctenitis**
E'. Minor axes decurrent; hairs simple: . . . **6. Dryopteris**

6. Blechnum Group : "Blechnaceae"

A.   Fronds dimorphic: . . . .   **1. Lorinseria**
A'. Fronds uniform: B, B'.
B.   Sori short, in chain-like rows: . . . . **2. Woodwardia**
B'. Sori elongate, continuous: . . . . . . **3. Blechnum**

7. Asplenium Group : "Aspleniaceae"

A single genus, **Asplenium**

8. Acrostichum Group : "Gymnogrammaceae"

A.   Fronds markedly dimorphic: . . . . **1. Stenochlaena**
A'. Fronds uniform: B, B'.
B.   Sporangia forming sheets, without wax: . **2. Acrostichum**
B'. Sporangia following veins and spreading between them,
     accompanied by white or yellow wax: C, C'.
C.   Pinnae divided on a digitate plan: . . . **3. Trismeria**
C'. Pinnae divided on a pinnate plan: . . **4. Pityrogramma**

9. Ceratopteris Group : "Parkeriaceae"

A single genus, **Ceratopteris**

10. Vittaria Group : "Vittariaceae"

A single genus, **Vittaria**

11. *Adiantum* Group : *"Adiantaceae"*

A single genus, *Adiantum*

12. *Cheilanthes* Group : *"Sinopteridaceae"*

A. Indusioid margins short green strips: . . 1. *Cheilanthes*
A′. Indusioid margins long scarious strips: B, B′.
B. Spore-bearing vein-tips free: . . . . . . 2. *Pellaea*
B′. Spore-bearing vein-tips connected by a cross-vein:
3. *Pteris*

13. *Nephrolepis* Group : *"Davalliaceae"*

A single genus, *Nephrolepis*

14. *Pteridium* Group : *"Pteridaceae"*

A single genus, *Pteridium*

15. *Dennstaedtia* Group : *"Dennstaedtiaceae"*

A. Sorus protected by a scarious flake: . . . 1. *Hypolepis*
A′. Sorus protected by an indusium: B, B′.
B. Indusium a flattened cone: . . . . . 2. *Sphenomeris*
B′. Indusium a shallow cup: . . . . . 3. *Dennstaedtia*

Most of the minor-family names above inserted in quotes after the group designations are those favored by Ching (1940). Since Copeland (1947) published his different plan in an impressive volume, he is more often followed; he frankly admitted, however, being unable to define such of his families as *"Pteridaceae"* and *"Aspidiaceae"* in a useful way, and few of his genus groupings have proved acceptable herein. Unfortunately, it seemed impracticable to delay the publication of this *Guide* until a generally satisfactory scheme of classification is worked out.

1. Common Fern Family : Keys to Species

1. *Polypodium* Group ("*Polypodiaceae*")

1:1. *Polypodium*

A. Blade densely scaly beneath: **1. *P. polypodioides*** (p. 60)
A'. Blade sparsely or not scaly beneath: B, B'.
B. Midrib bearing only hairs; segment-midveins barely curv-
ing out from it: . . . . . **2. *P. pectinatum*** (p. 62)
B'. Midrib bearing both hairs and scales; segment-midveins
long-curving out from it: . . . **3. *P. plumula*** (p. 64)

1:2. *Campyloneurum*

A. Blade linear, under 1 cm. broad, arching from crown:
1. *C. angustifolium* (p. 66)
A'. Blade elliptic-oblong, several cm. broad: B, B'.
B. Fronds arching, thick-textured; blade up to 30 cm. long,
with a tail-like tip: . . . . . **2. *C. costatum*** (p. 66)
B'. Fronds sub-erect, at maturity over 50 cm. long: C, C'.
C. Stipe around 1 cm. long; blade thick-textured, tapering
abruptly at both ends: . . . . . **3. *C. latum*** (p. 68)
C'. Stipe very short; blade thinnish-textured, tapering grad-
ually at both ends: . . . . . **4. *C. phyllitidis*** (p. 68)

1:3. *Microgramma* : One species, *M. heterophylla* (p. 70)

1:4. *Goniophlebium* : One species, *G. triseriale* (p. 72)

1:5. *Phymatodes* : One species, *P. scolopendria* (p. 64)

1:6. *Phlebodium* : One species, *P. aureum* (p. 74)

1:7. *Paltonium* : One species, *P. lanceolatum* (p. 76)

2. Woodsia Group ("Woodsiaceae")

2:1. *Onoclea* : One species, *O. sensibilis* (p. 78)

2:2. *Woodsia* : One species, *W. obtusa* (p. 80)

2:3. *Cystopteris* : One species, *C. protrusa* (p. 82)

3. *Thelypteris* Group ("*Thelypteridaceae*")

3:1. *Phegopteris* : One species, *P. hexagonoptera* (p. 84)

3:2. *Leptogramma* : One species, *L. pilosa* (p. 86)

3:3. *Meniscium*

A.   Pinna-margins finely serrate: .   .   **1.** *M. serratum* (p. 88)
A'. Pinna-margins entire: .   .   .   **2.** *M. reticulatum* (p. 88)

3:4. *Goniopteris*

A.   Blade reclining, often rooting: .   .   **3.** *G. reptans* (p. 94)
A'. Blade erect, not rooting: B, B'.
B.   Tip long-tapering: .   .   .   .   **1.** *G. sclerophylla* (p. 90)
B'. Tip a pinna-like segment: .   .   **2.** *G. tetragona* (p. 92)

3:5. *Cyclosorus*

A.   Pinna-lobes subtriangular: .   .   **1.** *C. gongylodes* (p. 96)
A'. Pinna-lobes oblong: B, B'.
B.   Blade long-tapering downward: .   **2.** *C. dentatus* (p. 98)
B'. Blade little tapering down: **3.** *C. quadrangularis* (p. 100)

3:6. *Thelypteris*

A.   Dimorphism distinct; sterile veins forked; margins of fertile segments reflexed: .   .   .   .   **1.** *T. palustris* (p. 102)
A'. Dimorphism obscure or none; veins mostly simple: B, B'.
B.   Blade-division 2-pinnate: .   .   **2.** *T. torresiana* (p. 104)
B'. Blade-division 1-pinnate: C, C'.
C.   Blade long-tapering downward: **3.** *T. resinifera* (p. 106)
C'. Blade little or not tapering downward: D, D'.
D.   Rootstock erect; scales broad, strongly reticulate; auricles elongate parallel to rachis: .   .   **4.** *T. patens* (p. 108)

D'. Rootstock creeping; scales and auricles otherwise: E, E'.

E. Blade-tip long-tailed, abrupt; pinnae *ca.* 1 cm. broad, barely auricled, the lobes acute: **5. T. augescens** (p. 110)

E'. Blade-tip short-tailed, gradual; pinnae to 2 cm. broad, diverging-auricled; lobes obtuse: **6. T. normalis** (p. 112)

3:6a. Thelypteris, supplement. The key to taxa 5 and 6 on the preceding page corresponds to average plants; there are also relatives which deviate to such an extent that they have received independent epithets.

A. Veins sporadically united to a 3-rayed star; spores aborted, so a hybrid: . . . . . **13. T. × versicolor** (p. 120)

A'. Veins all free: B, B'.

B. Mature fronds mostly over 50 cm. long; pinnae elongate; sori numerous: C, C'.

B'. Mature fronds mostly under 50 cm. long; pinnae short; sori few: E, E'.

C. Blade broadest well above base: . **9. v. harperi** (p. 114)

C'. Blade broadest at or near base: D, D'.

D. Pinnae straight; spores aborted, so a hybrid:
7. T. × lindheimeri (p. 110)

D'. Pinnae falcate; spores normal: . **8. T. "unca"** (p. 114)

E. Sori near mid-vein; pinnae spaced; blade-tip short and lobed (rare): . . . . . **10. T. "macilenta"** (p. 116)

E'. Sori near margins; pinnae close-set; blade-tip elongate with an entire tail: F, F'.

F. Rootstock elongate, penetrating moist humus (rare):
11. T. "macrorhizoma" (p. 116)

F'. Rootstock short, penetrating rock crevices (widespread):
12. T. "saxatilis" (p. 118)

4. *Athyrium* Group ("*Athyriaceae*")

4:1. *Diplazium*

A. Blade-division 2-pinnate: . . **1. D. esculentum** (p. 122)

A'. Blade-division 1-pinnate: B, B'.

B. Rachis hairy; blade triangular: **2. D. japonicum** (p. 124)

B'. Rachis glabrous; blade oblong:
3. D. lonchophyllum (p. 124)

4:2. *Athyrium*

A.   Blade-division 2-pinnate: .   1. *A. asplenioides* (p. 126)
A'. Blade-division 1-pinnate: B, B'.
B.   Pinnae entire, undulate: .   .   2. *A. pycnocarpon* (p. 128)
B'. Pinnae deeply lobed: .   .   3. *A. thelypterioides* (p. 128)

5. *Dryopteris* Group ("Aspidiaceae")

5:1. *Maxonia* : One species, *M. apiifolia* (p. 130)

5:2. *Cyrtomium* : One species, *C. falcatum* (p. 132)

5:3. *Polystichum* : One species, *P. acrostichoides* (p. 134)

5:4. *Tectaria*

A.   Blade small, oblong-triangular; indusium reniform: B, B'.
A'. Blade medium- to large-sized: C, C'.
B.   Blade-base a pair of slightly offset pinnae or mere lobes;
     veins coarse-areolate: .   .   .   .   1. *T. minima* (p. 136)
B'. Blade-base an offset pinna-pair; veins fine-areolate:
                                 2. *T.* × *amesiana* (p. 136)
C.   Herbage scaly; blade oblong; indusium reniform:
                                 3. *T. coriandrifolia* (p. 138)
C'. Herbage sparse-scaly; blade coarse, pentagonal; indusium
     peltate: .   .   .   .   .   .   4. *T. heracleifolia* (p. 138)

5:5. *Ctenitis*

A.   Scales red; divisions toothed: .   .   1. *C. ampla* (p. 140)
A'. Scales brown; divis. entire: 2. *C. submarginalis* (p. 140)

5:6. *Dryopteris*

A.   Fertile pinnae not contracted: .   .   3. *D. celsa* (p. 146)
A'. Fertile pinnae more or less contracted: B, B'.
B.   Contraction slight: .   .   .   .   2. *D.* × *australis* (p. 144)
B'. Contraction marked: .   .   .   1. *D. ludoviciana* (p. 142)

6. *Blechnum* Group ("*Blechnaceae*")

6:1. *Lorinseria* : One species, *L. areolata* (p. 148)

6:2. *Woodwardia*

A.   Pinna-lobes short, blunt: .   .   **1. *W. virginica*** (p. 150)
A'. Pinna-lobes long-acuminate: .   **2. *W. radicans*** (p. 152)

6:3. *Blechnum*

A.   Blade pinnate throughout; pinnae jointed to rachis, spaced, finely serrate: .   .   .   .   .   .   **1. *B. serrulatum*** (p. 154)
A'. Blade pinnate only below; pinnae sessile on rachis, close-set, entire: .   .   .   .   .   .   **2. *B. occidentale*** (p. 156)

7. *Asplenium* Group ("*Aspleniaceae*")

One genus, *Asplenium*

A.   Rachis dark brown to black: B, B'.
A'. Rachis (or midrib) green: E, E'.
B.   Fronds dimorphic, the fertile tall; pinnae alternate, serrate to incised: .   **1. *A. platyneuron*** (p. 158); (var. *b.,* p. 160)
B'. Fronds uniform; pinnae opposite to subopposite: C, C'.
C.   Sori few, toward lower margin: **2. *A. monanthes*** (p. 162)
C'. Sori multiple, on diverging veins: D, D'.
D.   Rootstock-scales conspicuous; upper pinna-margin obscurely toothed: .   .   .   .   .   .   **3. *A. resiliens*** (p. 164)
D'. Rootstock-scales obscure; upper pinna-margin manifestly toothed: .   .   .   .   .   .   **4. *A. heterochroum*** (p. 164)
E.   Blade simple, large, serrate; veins in close-set ascending rows: .   .   .   .   **5. *A. serratum*** (p. 166)
E'. Blade and veins otherwise: F, F'.
F.   Outline broad-triangular: G, G'.
F'. Outline narrow-triangular to elliptic or oblong: H, H'.
G.   Segments 3 to 5, obtuse to acutish: **6. *A. pumilum*** (p. 168)
G'. Segments 5 to 9, acute: .   **7. *v. anthriscifolium*** (p. 168)
H.   Division 1-pinnate: I, I'.
H'. Division 2- or 3-pinnate: K, K'.

I.   Pinna-outline obliquely rhombic: **8. A. dentatum** (p. 176)
I'. Pinna-outline elongate-triangular: J, J'.
J.   Auricles obscure; cutting fine: **9. A. abscissum** (p. 170)
J'. Auricles distinct; cutting coarse: **10. A. auritum** (p. 170)
K.   Stipe much shorter than blade: **11. A. verecundum** (p. 174)
K'. Stipe approaching blade in length: L, L'.
L.   Pinnae spreading, close-set; pinnules crowded, with nu-
     merous teeth and sori: .   .   .   **12. A. cristatum** (p. 172)
L'. Pinnae ascending: M, M'.
M.   Cutting of pinnules jagged, irregular; blade oblong:
                                    13. A. × biscayneanum (p. 176)
M'. Cutting of pinnules regular: N, N'.
N.   Pinnules broad, toothed: .   .   **14. A. × plenum** (p. 172)
N'. Pinnules narrow, finely cut: .   **15. A. × curtissii** (p. 174)

8. Acrostichum Group ("Gymnogrammaceae")

8:1. Stenochlaena

A.   Plant low-climbing; sterile pinnae oblong-elliptic, holly-
     like; fertile linear: .   .   .   .   **1. S. kunzeana** (p. 178)
A'. Plant high-climbing; sterile pinnae oblong, sharply ser-
     rate; fertile blade bipinnate: .   **2. S. tenuifolia** (p. 178)

8:2. Acrostichum

A.   Pinnae hairy beneath; vein-areoles fine, extending nearly
     perpendicular to midvein: .   .   **1. A. excelsum** (p. 180)
A'. Pinnae glabrous beneath; vein-areoles coarse, strongly in-
     clined upward: .   .   .   .   .   .   **2. A. aureum** (p. 180)

8:3. Pityrogramma : One species, P. calomelanos (p. 182)

8:4. Trismeria : One species, T. trifoliata (p. 184)

9. Ceratopteris Group ("Parkeriaceae")

One genus, Ceratopteris

A.   Plant tending to float free, buoyed up by inflated stipes;
     sterile blade pentagonal, deeply lobed; annulus barely de-
     veloped (widespread):   .   .   .   **1. C. pteridoides** (p. 186)

A'. Plant tending to remain rooted; stipes not inflated; sterile blade subtriangular, pinnately lobed; annulus well-developed (rare): . . . . **2. C. deltoidea** (p. 186)

10. *Vittaria* Group ("*Vittariaceae*")

One genus, *Vittaria*

A. Rootstock-scales strongly iridescent, their tip only one cell broad (widespread): . . . . **1. V. lineata** (p. 188)
A'. Rootstock-scales weakly iridescent, their tip several cells broad (rare): . . . . **2. V. filifolia** (p. 188)

11. *Adiantum* Group ("*Adiantaceae*")

One genus, *Adiantum*

A. Stipe arching: . . . . **1. A. capillus-veneris** (p. 190)
A'. Stipe ascending to erect: B, B'.
B. Tip of stipe branching into subequal curving rachises; pinnae oblong; blade fan-shaped: **3. A. pedatum** (p. 194)
B'. Tip of stipe not branching: C, C'.
C. Pinnae numerous; axes glabrous: **2. A. tenerum** (p. 192)
C'. Pinnae few, unsymmetrical: D, D'.
D. Axes fine-hairy; blade glabrous beneath; pinnules spreading: . . . . **4. A. melanoleucum** (p. 196)
D'. Axes, like blade beneath, copiously hairy; pinnules ascending: . . . . **5. A. hispidulum** (p. 196)

12. *Cheilanthes* Group ("*Sinopteridaceae*")

12:1. *Cheilanthes*

A. Fronds copiously hairy: . . . . **3. C. lanosa** (p. 200)
A'. Fronds sparsely hairy to glabrous: B, B'.
B. Axes dark brown; blade somewhat broadened at base, 3-pinnate below: . . . . **1. C. microphylla** (p. 198)
B'. Axes black; blade somewhat narrowed at base, 2-pinnate: **2. C. alabamensis** (p. 198)

12:2. *Pellaea* : One species, **P. atropurpurea** (p. 202)

12:3. *Pteris*

A.   Veins in part areolate: B, B'.

A'.   Veins all free: C, C'.

B.   Blade 3-pinnate: . . . . . **5. P. tripartita** (p. 212)

B'.   Blade 1-pinnate: . . . . . **6. P. grandifolia** (p. 212)

C.   Division pinnate throughout; blade-base narrow: D, D'.

C'.   Division pinnate above and pedate at broad base: E, E'.

D.   Stipe and rachis bearing copious persistent scales; blade markedly narrowed below; pinnae not jointed to rachis, manifestly serrate: . . . . . **1. P. vittata** (p. 204)

D'.   Stipe and rachis loose-scaly to glabrous; blade little narrowed below; pinnae jointed to rachis, obscurely serrate:
2. P. longifolia (p. 206)

E.   Segments barely decurrent; margins regularly serrate; veins perpendicular to midrib: . . . **3. P. cretica** (p. 208)

E'.   Segments markedly decurrent; margins irregularly serrate; veins sloping upward: . . . . **4. P. multifida** (p. 210)

13. *Davallia* Group ("*Davalliaceae*")

One genus, *Nephrolepis*

A.   Fronds up to several hundred cm. long; indusium with narrow sinus, the sporangia emerging all around it:
1. N. biserrata (p. 214)

A'.   Fronds mostly under 200 cm. long; indusium with broad sinus, the sporangia emerging at upper side: B, B'.

B.   Blade often over 50 cm. long and 8 broad; fronds arching (widespread): . . . . . . **2. N. exaltata** (p. 216)

B'.   Blade mostly under 50 cm. long and 7 broad; fronds erect (rare): C, C'.

C.   Tissue firm; veins obscure; tubers formed:
3. N. cordifolia (p. 216)

C'.   Tissue lax; veins manifest; tubers not formed:
4. N. pectinata (p. 214)

14. *Pteridium* Group ("*Pteridaceae*")

One genus, *Pteridium*

A. Pinnulets deeply cut into spaced narrow segments, conspicuously long-tailed: . . . 1. *P. caudatum* (p. 218)
A'. Pinnulets lobed: . . . . . 2. *P. aquilinum,* vars., B, B'.
B. Blade glabrous beneath; pinnule-tip *ca.* 8 times as long as broad: . . . . . 2a. v. *pseudocaudatum* (p. 220)
B'. Blade sparse-pubescent beneath; pinnule-tip *ca.* 4 times as long as broad: . . . . . 2b. v. *latiusculum* (p. 220)

15. *Dennstaedtia* Group ("*Dennstaedtiaceae*")

15:1. *Hypolepsis* : One species, *H. repens* (p. 222)

15:2. *Sphenomeris* : One species, *S. clavata* (p. 224)

15:3. *Dennstaedtia* : One species, *D. bipinnata* (p. 226)

2. Net Fern Family (*Gleicheniaceae*)

One genus and species, *Dicranopteris flexuosa* (p. 228)

3. Filmy Fern Family (*Hymenophyllaceae*)

A. Tissue 2 cells thick; margins bearing paired scales:

3:3. *Lecanium* : One species, *L. membranaceum* (p. 232)

A'. Tissue 1 cell thick; margins bearing hairs: B, B'.
B. Sheath pouch-like, deeply 2-parted; bristle short:

3:1. *Hymenophyllum* : One species, *H. tunbridgense* (p. 230)

B'. Sheath tubular to funnelform; bristle elongate:

3:2. *Trichomanes*

A. Sheath included, tipping midvein: . *T. petersii* (p. 232)
A'. Sheath exserted, 2-lipped: taxa 2 to 5; see text, p. 232, and figures, p. 233.

4. Climbing Fern Family (*Schizaeaceae*)

A. Fronds grass-like; fertile segments radiating:

4:1. *Actinostachys* : One species, **A. germani** (p. 234)

A'. Fronds with broad blade: B, B'.
B. Habit erect; blade triangular, pinnate; lowest pinna-pair long-stalked and fertile at tip:

4:2. *Anemia* : One species, **A. adiantifolia** (p. 236)

B'. Habit twining; blade oblong, complexly pinnate:

4:3. *Lygodium*

A. Sterile and fertile pinnae repeatedly divided into broad segments: . . . . **1. L. japonicum** (p. 238)
A'. Sterile pinnae forking into 2 hand-like divisions, fertile into narrow segments: . . . **2. L. palmatum** (p. 240)

5. Royal Fern Family (*Osmundaceae*)

One genus, *Osmunda*

A. Blade 1-pinnate, the pinnae lobed; sporangia borne on independent fronds: . . . . **1. O. cinnamomea** (p. 242)
A'. Blade 2-pinnate; sporangia borne on reduced terminal pinnules: . . . . **2. O. regalis** (p. 244)

6. Adders-tongue Family (*Ophioglossaceae*)

A. Plant a large epiphyte, with fan-like blade:

6:1. *Cheiroglossa* : One species, **C. palmata** (p. 246)

A'. Plant a small terrestrial herb: B, B'.
B. Blade simple; sporangia in 2 rows embedded below tip of fertile stalk: . . . . **6:2. Ophioglossum**
B'. Blade compound; sporangia in complex clusters at tip of fertile stalk: . . . . **6:3. Botrychium**

6:2. *Ophioglossum*

A. Veins in 2 series, with *ca.* 6-angled heavy areoles enclosing multiple lighter ones: .   .   .   **1. O. engelmanni** (p. 248)
A'. Veins not in 2 well-marked series: B, B'.
B. Size small, the height mostly under 5 cm.: C, C'.
B'. Size medium to large, mostly over 5 cm.: F, F'.
C. Mid-vein at blade-base heavy: D, D'.
C'. Mid-vein at blade-base like lateral ones: E, E'.
D. Areoles few, simple; blade ovate; rootstock globose:
2. O. mononeuron (p. 250)
D'. Areoles numerous, complex; blade elliptic; rootstock ellipsoid-ovoid: .   .   .   .   **3. O. dendroneuron** (p. 250)
E. Blade much longer than broad; rootstock ellipsoid:
4. O. tenerum (p. 250)
E'. Blade little longer than broad; rootstock globose:
5b. O. crotalophoroides v. nanum (p. 252)
F. Rootstock globose; blade concave:
5a. O crotalophoroides, type (p. 252)
F'. Rootstock ellipsoid; blade flattish: G, G'.
G. Roots often producing a new plant at tip; basal midvein heavy: .   .   .   .   **6. O. petiolatum** (p. 252)
G'. Roots rarely producing a new plant at tip; basal veins slender: .   .   .   .   **7. O. vulgatum** (p. 254)

6:3. *Botrychium*

A. Tissue deciduous; blade sessile or nearly so: B, B'.
A'. Tissue evergreen; blade long-stalked: C, C'.
B. Plant erect, vernal: .   .   .   **1. B. virginianum** (p. 256)
B'. Plant prostrate, autumnal: .   **2. B. lunarioides** (p. 258)
C. Blade-divisions many, close-set: **5. B. obliquum** (p. 262)
C'. Blade-divisions few, spaced: D, D'.
D. Pinnulets rounded: .   .   .   .   **3. B. alabamense** (p. 258)
D'. Pinnulets elongate: .   .   .   .   **4. B. biternatum** (p. 260)

7. Water-clover Family (*Marsileaceae*)

8. Floating Fern Family (*Salviniaceae*)

See text pages 264–66 and accompanying figures.

Lycosphens : Keys to Families and Genera

A. Roots lacking, the rootstock coral-like; stem wiry, bearing sparse scales; sporangia 3-lobed, in upper axils:
L 5. *Psilotum:* one species, *P. nudum* (p. 292)

A'. Roots developed; stem and sporangia otherwise: B, B'.

B. Stem ridged, hollow; green leaves lacking; sporangia short-lived: . . . . . . **1. Horsetail Family: L 1. *Equisetum***

B'. Stem not ridged, solid; green leaves present; sporangia long-lived: C, C'.

C. Plant sedge-like, the globose stem sending up quill-like leaves with sporangial base; spores of 2 sexes:
2. Quillwort Family: L 2. *Isoëtes*

C'. Plant moss-like, with elongate stem or branches: D, D'.

D. Sporangia borne in 4-sided cones; spores of 2 sexes:
3. Spike-moss Family: L 3. *Selaginella*

D'. Sporangia borne in cylindric cones or on leafy stems; spores uniform: . . . . **4. Clubmoss Family: L 4. *Lycopodium***

L 1. *Equisetum*

A. Stems dimorphic, sterile ones green and branched, fertile non-green and simple: . . **1. *E. arvense*** (upland only)

A'. Stems uniform, normally simple: B, B'.

B. Sheaths about as long as broad, not flaring; stem very rough: . . . . **2. *E. hyemale*** (p. 268)

B'. Sheaths longer than broad, flaring; stem barely rough:
3. *E.* × *ferrissi* (p. 268)

L 2. *Isoëtes*

A. Megaspores blackish, coarse-tubercled; plant tiny, in pools on granite hills: . . . . . **1. *I. melanospora*** (p. 272)

A'. Megaspores whitish; plant relatively large, not thus restricted: B, B'.

B. Surface honeycomb-reticulate: **2. *I. engelmanni*** (p. 272)

B'. Surface bearing tubercles: C, C'.

C. Tubercles many; plant-base dark:
3. *I. melanopoda* (p. 272)

C'. Tubercles few; plant-base pale: . **4. *I. flaccida*** (p. 270)

L 3. *Selaginella*

A. Tissue firm; leaves in many rows, all alike: B, B'.
A'. Tissue lax; leaves in 4 rows, the lateral larger: C, C'.
B. Leaf-bristles kinky (upland): . **1.** *S. tortipila* (p. 278)
B'. Leaf-bristles straight (lowland): **2.** *S. arenicola* (p. 280)
C. Stems slender; branching sparse (native): D, D'.
C'. Stems wiry; branching copious (naturalized): F, F'.
D. Leaf-margins thin, entire: . . . **3.** *S. apus* (p. 274)
D'. Leaf-margins thickened, finely serrate: E, E'.
E. Growth compact; lateral leaves acutish, crowded; cone *ca.* 3 to 5 mm. long: . . . . . **4.** *S. armata* (p. 276)
E'. Growth open; lateral leaves obtusish, spaced; cone *ca.* 5 to 10 mm. long: . . . . . **5.** *S. ludoviciana* (p. 276)
F. Habit vine-like: . . . . . **6.** *S. willdenovii* (p. 278)
F'. Habit spreading: G, G'.
G. Foliage iridescent blue-green: . **7.** *S. uncinata* (p. 278)
G'. Foliage light green: Various taxa (see text, p. 278)

L 4. *Lycopodium*

A. Habitat epiphytic; coneless: . **7.** *L. dichotomum* (p. 290)
A'. Habitat terrestrial; cones developed: B, B'.
B. Cones numerous, nodding: . . **1.** *L. cernuum* (p. 282)
B'. Cones solitary, tipping erect branches: C, C'.
C. Branch-leaves small, spaced: **2.** *L. carolinianum* (p. 284)
C'. Branch-leaves relatively large, crowded: D, D'.
D. Leaves appressed; cone 5 mm. thick:
3. *L. appressum* (p. 284)
D'. Leaves spreading; cone over 8 mm. thick: E, E'.
E. Stem arching, rooting at ends; branches 8 to 15 and cone 13 to 25 mm. thick: . . . **5.** *L. alopecuroides* (p. 288)
E'. Stem prostrate, rooting all along: F, F'.
F. Branches 4 to 8 and cone 10 to 20 mm. thick:
4. *L. prostratum* (p. 286)
F'. Branches 3 to 6 and cone 8 to 15 mm. thick:
6. *L. chapmani* (p. 288)

L 5. *Psilotum*

A single species, *P. nudum* (p. 292)

DESCRIPTIONS AND
ILLUSTRATIONS

PLAN OF SPECIES TREATMENT

Each species herein treated is first assigned a colloquial name; since many of them are not sufficiently conspicuous to have received a real "common name," these have been frankly coined by translating the technical ones, or with reference to some notable feature. The accepted technical name-combination is then added, so that there can be no question as to what taxon is referred to. Descriptive data are presented in separate paragraphs:

FEATURES: Here are given details as to significant characters, including dimensions of fronds. The values stated are those most frequently encountered; in especially favorable places the plants may grow larger, in barren ones they may be dwarfed.

RANGE: This covers primarily "our region," namely the southeastern lowlands, although certain taxa of the uplands which do not occur in the northeastern states are included. Extralimital ranges are briefly stated, in brackets.

HABITAT: Under this are characterized the sorts of places where the species usually grows; occasional extensions into other situations are of course to be expected.

CULTURE: A general discussion of this is given in the introductory pages, but notes on individual species are added here. "Not cultivated" refers only to ordinary gardens; specialists may be growing all taxa.

NOMENCLATURE: The name-combination selected for adoption is given first, in bold-face type. Then to enable users of other fern books to recognize the equivalents of the names they may find therein, a list of all frequently encountered alternatives is added in italics. Since Small's *Ferns of the Southeastern States* (1938) is widely used in our region, the names accepted in that work are indicated by (S).

1. Common Fern Family : *Polypodiàceae*

ROCK-CAP FERNS : *POLYPÒDIUM*

In allusion to the way the rootstock seemed to walk over surfaces, the European representatives of this genus were early termed polypodium, from the Greek for many feet, and this was made a genus name by Linnaeus in 1753.

Notable genus characters comprise the conspicuous jointing of spaced fronds to a scaly rootstock, the presence in the stipe of 3 upwardly united vascular strands, the division of the firm evergreen blade into long pinna-like segments, and the lack of indusium on the large round sori. Only free-veined taxa are here retained in the genus, those with areolate veins being assigned to minor genera. The basal chromosome number is 37.

Resurrection Fern : *Polypòdium polypodioìdes*

FEATURES: Stipe *ca.* 4 to 8 cm. long, bearing, as does the underside of the blade, copious peltate scales. Blade *ca.* 6 to 12 cm. long and 2 to 4 broad. The colloquial name refers to the way the fronds curl up when dry, but revive when moistened again.

RANGE: Throughout our region and somewhat farther north. [Represented in trop. Amer. by minor varieties.]

HABITAT: Perched on trees and sprawling over rocks. Soil varying from decidedly acid to circumneutral.

CULTURE: Often grown on pieces of wood or humus hummocks.

NOMENCLATURE:

Polypodium polypodioides Watt, 1866.
(*Acrostichum polypodioides* L., 1753, basionym.)
Marginaria polypodioides Tidestrom, 1905. (S)
P. polypodioides var. *michauxianum* Weatherby, 1929.

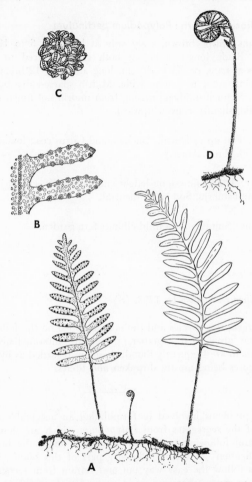

RESURRECTION FERN : *Polypodium polypodioides*

A. Plant, reduced.   B. Segments.   C. Sorus, enlarged.
D. Frond in dry weather.

Comb Rock-cap Fern : *Polypòdium pectinàtum*

FEATURES: Stipe brown, scaly only at base, *ca.* 6 to 12 cm. long. Blade long-tapering at both ends, reduced to mere wings at base, *ca.* 35 to 70 cm. long and 6 to 12 broad, the segments *ca.* 4 to 8 mm. wide. Midrib sparse-hairy but not scaly. Segment-midvein arising from midrib not much below middle, slightly convex upward.

RANGE: Fla. up to Duval, Alachua, and Citrus cos.; found here in 1873. [Trop. Amer.]

HABITAT: Damp limestone ledges and sink walls, clayey banks, logs and stumps. Soil circumneutral.

CULTURE: Suitable for a mild-climate fern garden.

NOMENCLATURE:

Polypodium pectinatum L., 1753. (S)

Wherever this species and the one described on the following text-page grow near together, perplexing intermediates between them are frequently found; these are regarded as hybrids, their spores being mostly shrunken and lifeless.

The problems involved in formulating an acceptable treatment of the segregates from *Polypodium* which are described on several following pages were discussed under the heading "Classification" in the introductory part of this *Guide*. Some workers follow the easy way out and refrain from recognizing the minor genera; however, as in our region these differ widely in aspect, it has seemed preferable to accept them here. Similar choices have had to be made again and again among our southern lowland taxa. Whether to recognize single comprehensive "super-genera" or multiple minor ones is a matter of viewpoint; it will soon become evident to the user of this *Guide* that its author favors on the whole the second plan.

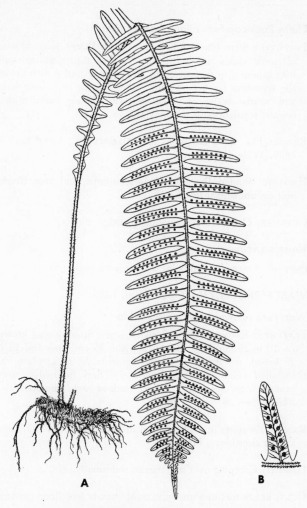

COMB ROCK-CAP FERN : *Polypodium pectinatum*

A. Plant, reduced.   B. Segment.

Plumy Rock-cap Fern : *Polypòdium plùmula*

FEATURES: Stipe blackish brown, *ca.* 6 to 12 cm. long, bearing
  scattered scales and hairs. Blade rather abrupt at base and
  long-tapering to tip, *ca.* 20 to 40 cm. long and 3 to 6 broad,
  the segments *ca.* 2 to 4 mm. wide. Midrib with both hairs
  and sparse scales. Segment-midvein arising from midrib
  toward segment-base, strongly convex.

RANGE: Fla. up to St. Johns and Alachua cos.; found here in
  1839. [Widespread in trop. Amer.]

HABITAT: Shaded limestone ledges, stumps, and tree trunks.
  Soil circumneutral to subacid.

CULTURE: Desirable as a woodland garden subject.

NOMENCLATURE:

Polypodium plumula Humboldt & Bonpland, 1810. (S)

WART FERNS : *PHYMATÒDES* Presl, 1836.

Wart Fern : *Phymatòdes scolopéndria*

FEATURES: Rootstock slender, sparse-scaly. Stipe shining brown,
  ~~*ca.* 10 to 20 cm. long. Blade *ca.* 18 to 35 cm. long and 13 to~~
  25 broad, cut into few coarse segments. Veins areolate, the
  included veinlets with enlarged tip. Sori in medial rows,
  sunken in areoles with a "wart" back of each. (Figured with
  Phlebodium aureum, p. 75.)

RANGE: Escaping in s. Fla.; found in Manatee Co. in 1937, now
  known elsewhere. [Trop. Asia.]

HABITAT: Creeping over tree trunks; soil usually acid.

CULTURE: Sometimes grown in mild-climate woodland gardens.

NOMENCLATURE:

Phymatodes scolopendria Ching, 1933.
(*Polypodium scolopendria* Burman, 1768, basionym.)
Polypodium phymatodes L., 1771.

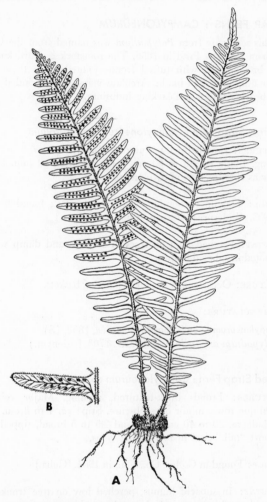

PLUMY ROCK-CAP FERN : *Polypodium plumula*

A. Plant, reduced.   B. Segment.

STRAP FERNS : *CAMPYLONEÙRUM*

This segregate from *Polypodium* was named from the Greek for bent veins by Presl in 1836. The rootstock is short, knobby, and brown-scaly, with tufted fronds jointed to it; these have a smooth, strap-like blade. Areolate veins have included vein-lets bearing round sori lacking indusium.

Narrow Strap Fern : *Campyloneùrum angustifòlium*

FEATURES: Fronds thick-textured, arching. Stipe *ca.* 3 to 5 cm. long. Blade *ca.* 30 to 60 cm. long and 5 to 10 mm. broad. Veins obscure. Sori in two long rows.

RANGE: Fla. up to Seminole and Collier cos.; found here in 1903. [Widespread in trop. Amer.]

HABITAT: Perched high on trees in swamps and damp woods; rooted in subacid humus.

CULTURE: Occasionally grown in hanging baskets.

NOMENCLATURE:

Campyloneurum ("-on") angustifolium Fée, 1852. (S)
(*Polypodium angustifolium* Swartz, 1788, basionym.)

Tailed Strap Fern : *Campyloneùrum costàtum*

FEATURES: Fronds thick-textured, arching. Major veins in oblique rows; minor ones obscure. Stipe *ca.* 4 to 8 cm. long. Blade *ca.* 20 to 40 cm. long and 2.5 to 5 broad, tipped by a short "tail." Sori in rows along veins.

RANGE: Found in Collier Co., Fla., in 1904. [Cuba.]

HABITAT: In subacid humus, perched low on tree trunks and on "knees" in wet woods. Not cultivated.

NOMENCLATURE:

Campyloneurum costatum Presl, 1836. (S)
(*Polypodium costatum* Kunze, 1834, basionym.)

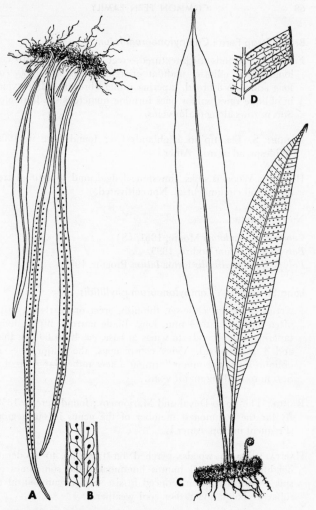

NARROW STRAP-FERN : *Campyloneurum angustifolium*
A. Plant, reduced.   B. Portion of blade, enlarged.

TAILED STRAP-FERN : *Campyloneurum costatum*
C. Plant, reduced.   D. Portion of blade.

Broad Strap Fern : *Campyloneùrum làtum*

FEATURES: Fronds thick-textured, erect. Stipe *ca.* 5 to 10 cm.
long. Blade elliptic, undulate-margined, *ca.* 40 to 80 cm.
long and 4 to 8 broad, tapering rather abruptly. Major veins
in oblique rows; minor ones forming numerous small areoles.
Sori in rows along major veins.

RANGE: S. Fla. up to Highlands Co.; found here in 1903.
[Widespread in trop. Amer.]

HABITAT: Wooded sinks, limestone ledges, and sometimes tree .
bases. Soil circumneutral. Not cultivated.

NOMENCLATURE:

Campyloneurum latum Moore, 1861. (S)
Polypodium latum Sodiro, 1893.
Polypodium phyllitidis forma *latum* Proctor, 1953.

Long Strap Fern : *Campyloneùrum phyllítidis*

FEATURES: Fronds close-set, thinnish, erect or nearly so. Stipe
often only *ca.* 2 to 4 mm. long. Blade narrow-elliptic, long-
tapering at both ends, to wings at base, *ca.* 40 to 80 cm. long
and 4 to 8 broad. Veins conspicuous, the major ones in
oblique rows, the minor forming a few rather large areoles.
Sori in rows along major veins.

RANGE: Fla. up to Duval and Marion cos.; found here in 1838.
By far the commonest member of the genus in our region.
[Frequent in trop. Amer.]

HABITAT: Damp woods, perched on trees up to moderate
heights, on logs and humus hummocks, and sometimes on
sink walls, then often reduced in size. Soil circumneutral to
subacid. Tolerating rather cool weather.

CULTURE: Desirable for shady gardens in pen. Fla.

NOMENCLATURE:

Campyloneurum phyllitidis Presl, 1836.
(*Polypodium phyllitidis* L., 1753, basionym.)

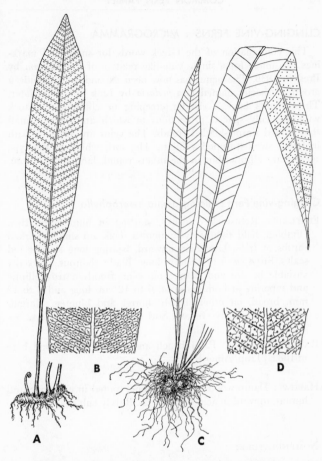

BROAD STRAP-FERN : *Campyloneurum latum*

A. Plant, reduced. B. Portion of blade.

LONG STRAP-FERN : *Campyloneurum phyllitidis*

C. Plant, reduced. D. Portion of blade.

CLINGING-VINE FERNS : *MICROGRÁMMA*

This combination of the Greek words for small and markings was made for a single vine-like relative of *Polypodium* by Presl in 1836. The genus has now been expanded to include a group of species named *Craspedaria* by Link five years later. These plants have a slender creeping or climbing rootstock with unevenly spaced projections to which are jointed small short-stiped simple-bladed fronds. The veins are areolate, with included swollen-tipped veinlets. The sori, which in the type species are elliptic, but in the others round, lack an indusium.

Clinging-vine Fern : *Micrográmma heterophýlla*

FEATURES: Rootstock cord-like, starting in humus and then climbing, held tightly by numerous roots, up smooth-barked shrubs or trees, branching upward, bearing long slender red scales. Stipe *ca.* 5 to 10 mm. long. Blade glabrous, markedly variable in size and shape: on some fronds narrow-elliptic and tapering at both ends, *ca.* 6 to 12 cm. long and 6 to 12 mm. broad, on others much shorter and blunter. Margins entire or shallowly crenate. Sori spaced in medial rows.

RANGE: Fla. up to Palm Beach and Collier cos.; found here in 1882. [Trop. Amer.]

HABITAT: Damp woods over limestone, rooted in circumneutral humus, upward in acid bark-debris. Rarely cult'd.

NOMENCLATURE:

Microgramma heterophylla Wherry, p. 346.
(*Polypodium heterophyllum* L., 1753, basionym.)
Polypodium exiguum Heward, 1838.
Polypodium swartzii Baker, 1868.
Phymatodes heterophyllum Small, 1932. (S)
Microsorium heterophyllum Hawkes, 1951.
Craspedaria heterophylla ("-um") Diddell, 1958.
     Still other synonyms have been published, this fern having been renamed more than any other in our region.

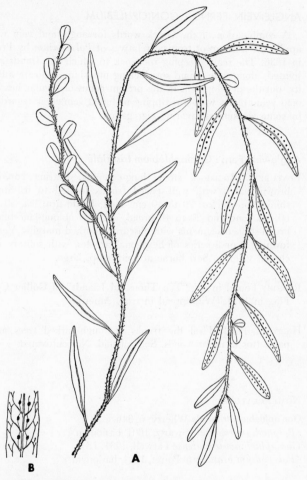

CLINGING-VINE FERN : *Microgramma heterophylla*

A. Plant, reduced.   B. Portion of blade.

ANGLE-VEIN FERNS : *GONIOPHLÈBIUM*

A combination of the Greek words for angle and vein was applied to a group of tropical relatives of *Polypodium* by Presl in 1836. The scaly creeping rootstock to which the fronds are jointed, along with round sori lacking indusium, indicate affinity, but the development in the present genus of regular hexagonal vein-areoles with sori tipping included veinlets is regarded by some workers as favoring segregation.

Angle-vein Fern : *Goniophlèbium triseriàlè*

FEATURES: Rootstock stout, long-creeping, bearing copious brown scales, with well-spaced fronds jointed to it. Stipe shining brown, *ca.* 20 to 40 cm. long. Blade firm, *ca.* 30 to 60 cm. long and 20 to 40 broad, cut into oblong-lanceolate broad-stalked segments with obscurely toothed margins. Veins forming 2 or 3 series of hexagonal areoles, with solitary included veinlets. Sori borne at veinlet-tip, large.

RANGE: Found in the "Ten Thousand Islands" of Collier Co., Fla., in 1924. [Widespread in trop. Amer.]

HABITAT: Perched on the trunks of rough-barked trees and palmettos in moist woods. Soil subacid. Not cultivated.

NOMENCLATURE:

Goniophlebium triseriale Wherry, p. 346.
(*Polypodium triseriale* Swartz, 1801, basionym.)
Goniophlebium brasiliense Farwell, 1931. (S)
(*Polypodium brasiliense* Poiret, 1804, basionym.)

There is some question as to whether this and related tropical American taxa really belong to the same (minor) genus as the Asiatic ones to which the name *Goniophlebium* was originally applied. This and other nomenclatorial problems could be settled by returning a series of genera here recognized to a supergenus, *Polypodium*.

ANGLE-VEIN FERN : *Goniophlebium triseriale*

A. Plant, reduced.　B. Portion of a segment.

SERPENT FERNS : *PHLEBÒDIUM*

This colloquial name refers to the snake-like aspect of the rootstock as it winds through supporting material. The technical name, from the Greek for prominent veins, was proposed by Robert Brown, according to John Smith, 1842.

The plants are mostly epiphytic, with a creeping scaly rootstock, to which rather large fronds are jointed. The blade is cut into few coarse segments or lobes. There are numerous areolate veins, with two free veinlets included in medial areoles. The sori are elevated, in major areoles, forming 1 or 2 somewhat uneven rows.

Goldfoot Fern : *Phlebòdium aùreum*

FEATURES: Rootstock *ca.* 8 to 15 mm. thick, its copious long-tapering ciliate reddish scales producing in mass a golden sheen. Fronds spaced, gracefully arching. Stipe stout, shining brown, *ca.* 15 to 30 cm. long. Blade at first bluish but becoming yellowish green, *ca.* 30 to 60 cm. long and 20 to 40 broad, cut into a few coarse segments or lobes. Sori prominent.

RANGE: Fla. up to Nassau and Dixie cos., and rarely to Glynn Co., Ga.; found in Fla. in 1838, in Ga. not until 1950. [Widespread over trop. Amer.]

HABITAT: Rootstock winding through old leaf-bases of palmettos, rough oak bark, and crumbly limestone. Soil subacid to circumneutral. The fronds are wilted by frost, but the rootstock may survive. Can withstand considerable sunlight if the surrounding air is moist.

CULTURE: Much grown in Fla. gardens (and northern greenhouses), in several horticultural forms.

NOMENCLATURE:

Phlebodium aureum John Smith, 1842. (S)
(*Polypodium aureum* L., 1753, basionym.)

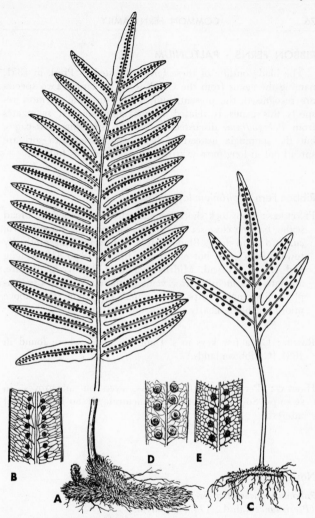

GOLD-FOOT FERN : *Phlebodium aureum*

A. Plant, reduced.   B. Portion of a segment.

WART-FERN : *Phymatodes scolopendria* (p. 64)

C. Plant, reduced.   Segment: D. upper and E. lower side.

RIBBON FERNS : *PALTÒNIUM*

The blade outline of these ferns suggested to Presl, in 1851, naming the genus from the Greek word for lance. Two species are recognized, the present, and another in Asia. In most respects this genus is related to the simple-bladed segregates from *Polypodium,* discussed on several preceding text-pages, but the sporangia instead of being aggregated into sori are spread out in long narrow strips. Our species is as follows:

Ribbon Fern : *Paltònium lanceolàtum*

FEATURES: Rootstock short-creeping, densely clothed by broad scales, bearing close-set firm fronds jointed to it. Stipe brown, *ca.* 2 to 4 cm. long. Blade simple, entire, tapering gradually toward both ends, but obtusish at tip, *ca.* 18 to 35 cm. long and 1.5 to 3 broad. Midrib prominent, but veins obscure, areolate with included free veinlets, the outer areoles incomplete. Sporangial strips submarginal, extending from above middle of blade nearly but not quite to tip.

RANGE: On a few keys in s. Dade Co., Fla., where found in 1881. [Caribbean lands.]

HABITAT: Perched on tree trunks, even on mangroves, in swamps. Soil subacid to circumneutral. Of no horticultural interest.

NOMENCLATURE:

Paltonium lanceolatum Presl, 1851. (S)
(*Pteris lanceolata* L., 1753, basionym.)
Cheilogramma lanceolata Underwood, 1900.

In the 50-year interval between the proposal of the two recombinations listed above, this fern got assigned to 9 or 10 other genera; none of the resulting names, however, came into general use.

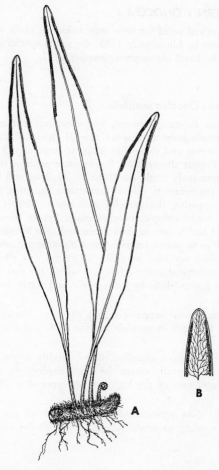

RIBBON-FERN : *Paltonium lanceolatum*

A. Plant, reduced.   B. Blade-tip.

BEAD FERN : ONOCLÈA

This ancient word for some now unknown plant was made a genus name by Linnaeus in 1753; the single species is described below. The basal chromosome number is 37.

Bead Fern : *Onoclèa sensibilis*

FEATURES: Rootstock coarse, long-creeping near ground surface, sending up a close-set row of moderate-sized fronds. Stipe brown and somewhat scaly at base, *ca.* 25 to 50 cm. long. Fronds dimorphic: Sterile ones with a thickish but deciduous leafy blade *ca.* 20 to 40 cm. long and broad, pinnately cut nearly to midrib into coarse segments, at least the lower opposite, the margins undulate to deeply lobed but entire. Veins conspicuously areolate. Fertile ones arising in autumn and becoming dark green and then brown, so firm in texture as to persist for two years, bipinnate; pinnules roundish, rolling up into bead-like structures (to which the favored colloquial name refers), in which the sori are hidden. Fronds intermediate between sterile and fertile occasional.

RANGE: Scattered over our region, down to Alachua Co., Fla. [More frequent in uplands and ne. U.S. and Can.]

HABITAT: Meadows, marshes, shores, muddy slopes, and moist situations generally where the soil is moderately acid. Seemingly intolerant of the high temperatures of s. Fla.

CULTURE: Not recommended, since after all not attractive, and spreading so pervasively as to overwhelm more delicate plants.

NOMENCLATURE:

Onoclea sensibilis L., 1753. (S)
   INTERMEDIATE-FROND STATE:
O. sensibilis f. *obtusilobata* Gilbert, 1901.
(*O. obtusilobata* Schkuhr, 1809, basionym.)

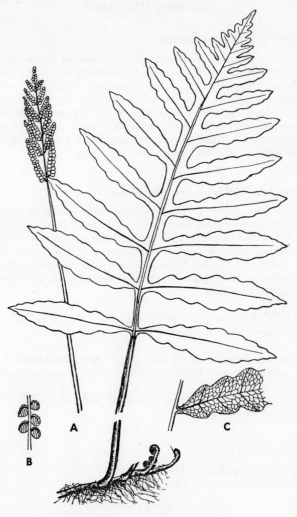

BEAD-FERN : *Onoclea sensibilis*

A. Plant with fertile and sterile fronds, reduced.
B. Fertile pinnules.   C. Base of sterile segment.

CLIFF FERNS : WOÒDSIA

This genus name was first validly published by Robert Brown in 1813, in honor of a friend. Its members are rather small plants, with a short scaly-tipped rootstock, sending up a tuft of fronds from a mass of stubble representing past season's stipe-bases. The pinnae are deeply lobed. The round sori have attached beneath a cup-like indusium, which soon splits into segments. The basal chromosome number is 41. Most species are northern, but one extends into our region:

Blunt-lobe Cliff Fern : Woòdsia obtùsa

FEATURES: Fertile fronds deciduous, sterile evergreen, mostly smaller; the former have: Stipe *ca.* 10 to 20 cm. long, brown below and yellowish upward, somewhat scaly but tending to become glabrous at maturity. Blade *ca.* 15 to 30 cm. long and 6 to 12 broad, bearing on axes beneath minute glands and small pale scales. Indusium segments broad, at maturity spreading-stellate.

RANGE: Relatively rare in our region, sw. Ga. to e. Tex. and northw. [More frequent in s. uplands and n. states.]

HABITAT: Wooded bluffs and slopes. Soil circumneutral to moderately acid. Intolerant of high summer temperatures.

CULTURE: Of little ornamental value and not known to be grown in our region.

NOMENCLATURE:

Woodsia obtusa Torrey, 1840. (S)
(*Polypodium obtusum* Sprengel, 1804, basionym.)

This genus is related to *Dryopteris,* with which it agrees in chromosome number, but is here placed in a separate group because of its unique indusial features. On the other hand, it is associated with the dissimilar genus *Onoclea,* the indusium of which is likewise inferior.

BLUNT-LOBE CLIFF-FERN : *Woodsia obtusa*

A. Plant, reduced.   B. Pinna-base.   C. Sorus, enlarged.

BLADDER FERNS : *CYSTÓPTERIS*

The Greek words for bladder and fern, in reference to a somewhat bladder-like indusium, were combined to form a genus name by Bernhardi in 1806. Most of the members are northern, but one ranges south into our region along the Mississippi Valley.

The plants are rather small ferns with a slender stipe enclosing two vascular strands. The tissue is delicate, and the blades are cut in a lacy pattern. The sori are round, and the indusium, which tends to be short-lived, is attached to a vein at the inner base. Although not very similar, this genus is generally held to be closely related to the Lady Ferns (*Athyrium*). The basal chromosome number is 42.

Lowland Brittle Fern : *Cystópteris protrùsa*

FEATURES: Rootstock slender, creeping, hairy, growing during the season several cm. beyond the short row of fronds. Stipe *ca.* 13 to 25 cm. long, green and glabrous, except for sparse loose basal scales. Blade *ca.* 13 to 25 cm. long and 6 to 12 broad, 2-pinnate, narrowed at base. Indusium truncate at tip.

RANGE: In our region known from c. Ala. to e. Tex. and northw. [Widespread in uplands and n. U.S.]

HABITAT: Chiefly on thinly wooded slopes and flats; soil circumneutral and rich in humus and mineral nutrients.

CULTURE: Can be grown in a woodland fern garden, spreading by rootstocks into large patches. While appearing early in spring, tends to wither during hot weather.

NOMENCLATURE:

Cystopteris protrusa Blasdell, 1960.
(*C. fragilis* var. *protrusa* Weatherby, 1935, basionym.)

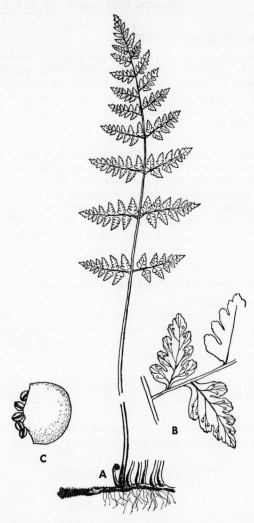

LOWLAND BRITTLE-FERN : *Cystopteris protrusa*

A. Plant, reduced.   B. Pinnules.   C. Sorus, enlarged.

BEECH FERNS : *PHEGÓPTERIS*

While the earliest name for this group of ferns was *Gymno-carpium,* published by Newman in 1851, it has become customary to use instead *Phegopteris,* from Greek words for beech and fern, proposed by Fée in 1852. Some workers decline to segregate it from the complex genus *Thelypteris,* but it is here considered distinct.

The long cord-like scaly rootstock sends up a row of moderate-sized deciduous fronds, the fertile late in the season. The stipe contains two vascular strands which unite upward. The blade is triangular with pinna-like segments or one basal pinna-pair; the axes beneath bear fine hairs and sparse scales. The sori are small and round and lack an indusium. The basal chromosome number is 30. One species enters our region:

Southern Beech Fern : *Phegópteris hexagonóptera*

FEATURES: Stipe *ca.* 20 to 40 cm. long, sparse-hairy. Blade *ca.* 15 to 30 cm. long and 18 to 35 broad, deeply cut into segments with basal angled wings; in our region the lower pair is sometimes set off by a strip of bare rachis several mm. long, thus constituting pinnae.

RANGE: Scattered from Liberty Co., Fla., to e. Tex. and northw. [Commoner in s. upl., ne. states, and se. Can.]

HABITAT: Wooded slopes in somewhat acid humus-rich soil. Intolerant of high summer temperatures.

CULTURE: Desirable in a cool woodland garden.

NOMENCLATURE:

Phegopteris hexagonoptera Fée, 1852. (S)
(*Polypodium hexagonopterum* Michaux, 1803, basionym.)
Dryopteris hexagonoptera Christensen, 1905.
Thelypteris hexagonoptera Weatherby, 1919.

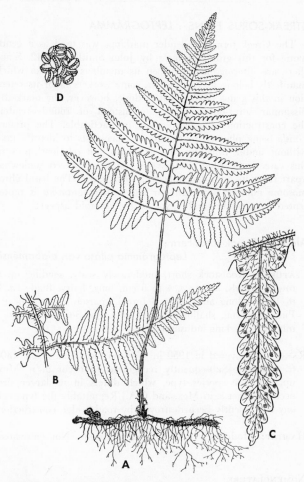

SOUTHERN BEECH-FERN : *Phegopteris hexagonoptera*

A. Plant, reduced.   B. Basal division.   C. Segment,
enlarged.   D. Sorus, enlarged.

STREAK-SORUS FERNS : *LEPTOGRÁMMA*

The Greek term for slender markings was used as a genus name for this group of ferns by John Smith in 1842. Since there are intermediates between its members and taxa which manifestly belong to *Thelypteris,* some workers favor its retention in this genus. When that is done, however, the markedly dissimilar sorus-outline—elongate instead of round—renders the construction of a simple key impracticable. The present *Guide* being planned to enable non-specialists to identify taxa without undue difficulty, however, phyletic relationship is in this case disregarded, and *Leptogramma* is placed somewhat apart from its admitted ancestor, *Thelypteris.* The basal chromosome number is 36. In our region *Leptogramma* is represented by a rather small taxon of thelypteroid aspect:

Alabama Streak-sorus Fern :
Leptográmma pilòsa var. alabaménsis

FEATURES: Rootstock short, moderately scaly, sending up a row of fronds. Stipe *ca.* 4 to 8 cm. long, hairy. Blade *ca.* 8 to 15 cm. long and 1.5 to 3 broad, sparsely hairy beneath. Pinnae oblong, shallowly lobed, bluntish. Sori linear, *ca.* 5 mm. long, lacking indusium.

RANGE: Discovered in 1950 in Winston Co., Ala., at *ca.* 1300 ft. altitude. [Subsequently recognized to occur in n. Mex. uplands; the species type, which differs in its larger size, occurs farther s. in Mex. and C.A.] Regrettably the type colony has recently been destroyed by road-bridge construction.

HABITAT: Moderately acid soil on sandstone. Not cultivated.

NOMENCLATURE:

Leptogramma pilosa Underwood, 1902.
(*Gymnogramme pilosa* Martens & Galeotti, 1842, basionym.)
Lastrea pilosa Copeland, 1947.
Thelypteris pilosa Crawford, 1951.
Leptogramma pilosa var. alabamensis Wherry, p. 346.
(*T. pilosa* var. *alabamensis* Crawford, 1951, basionym.)

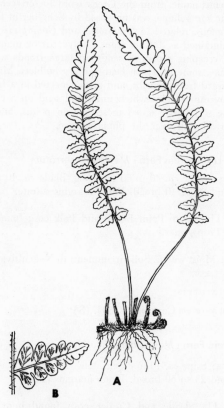

ALABAMA STREAK-SORUS FERN :
Leptogramma pilosa var. alabamensis

A. Plant, reduced.   B. Pinna.

LATTICE-VEIN FERNS : *MENÍSCIUM*

This genus name, from the Greek word for crescent in allusion to the sorus-shape, was proposed by Schreber in 1791. It is a minor genus, related to *Cyclosorus* and *Goniopteris,* but like them maintained as distinct from *Thelypteris* by many specialists. The creeping rootstock sends up large fronds with alternate pinnae, some of which bear axillary bulblets. Major veins slope upward from midribs, and are connected in a lattice-like pattern by minor veins which unite and send up a compound vein. The sori curve across these tri-vein points, and at maturity spread well over the pinna surface.

Toothed Lattice-vein Fern : *Meniscium serràtum*

FEATURES: Stipe *ca.* 40 to 80 cm. long. Blade *ca.* 40 to 80 cm. long and 20 to 40 broad. Pinna margins serrate.

RANGE: Fla. up to Palm Beach and Polk cos.; found here in 1912. [Trop. Amer.]

HABITAT: Moist woods. Soil circumneutral. Not cultivated.

NOMENCLATURE:

Meniscium serratum Cavanilles, 1803. (S)

Lattice-vein Fern : *Meniscium reticulàtum*

FEATURES: Stipe *ca.* 40 to 80 cm. long. Blade *ca.* 50 to 100 cm. long and 25 to 50 broad. Pinna margins entire.

RANGE: Fla., Dade and Collier cos.; found here in 1903. [Caribbean lands.]

HABITAT: Perched on cypress knees and low on tree trunks in swamps. Soil somewhat acid. Not cultivated.

NOMENCLATURE:

Meniscium reticulatum Swartz, 1801. (S)
(*Polypodium reticulatum* L., 1759, basionym.)

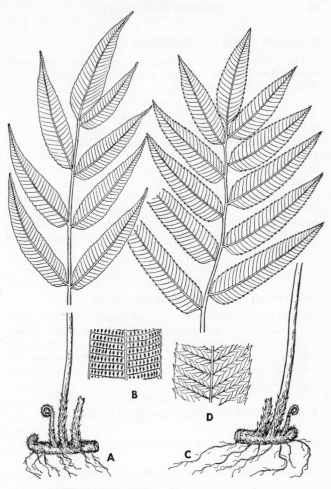

LATTICE-VEIN FERN : *Meniscium reticulatum*

A. Plant, reduced.   B. Section of a pinna.

TOOTHED LATTICE-VEIN FERN : *Meniscium serratum*

C. Plant, reduced.   D. Section of a pinna.

STAR-HAIR FERNS : *GONIÓPTERIS*

The union of the inner pinna-veins in a conspicuous angle suggested to Presl, in 1836, the naming of this group of ferns from the Greek words for angle and fern. This feature is the same as that which has led to separation of other minor genera from *Thelypteris;* but in the present group there is an additional differentiating character—the presence, on the tissues, of hairs which branch in a starry pattern. Admittedly, there are species of *Thelypteris* which have the same sort of hairs, and this leads some workers to refuse to accept the generic independence of *Goniopteris.* As, however, several leading fern specialists do recognize it, and even refer to the veining pattern when it appears in other taxa as "goniopteroid," it is here treated as a (minor) genus. The general features are the same as in *Cyclosorus* and *Thelypteris.* Basal chromosome number is 36.

Stiff Star-hair Fern : *Goniópteris sclerophýlla*

FEATURES: Rootstock stout, erect, extending several cm. above ground, bearing glossy brown stellate-haired scales. Fronds clustered, stiffly erect. Stipe *ca.* 8 to 15 cm. long. Blade dull green, rigid, tapering downward, *ca.* 20 to 40 cm. long and 8 to 15 broad. Pinnae cordate, deeply cut, the lobes with broad triangular tip. Sori medial.

RANGE: S. Dade Co., Fla., where found in 1940. [W.I.]

HABITAT: In damp woods around sinks; soil circumneutral.

CULTURE: Sometimes grown in subtropical fern gardens.

NOMENCLATURE:

Goniopteris sclerophylla Wherry, p. 346.
(*Aspidium sclerophyllum* Poeppig *ex* Kunze, 1827, basionym.)
Dryopteris sclerophylla Christensen, 1911.
Thelypteris sclerophylla Morton, 1951.

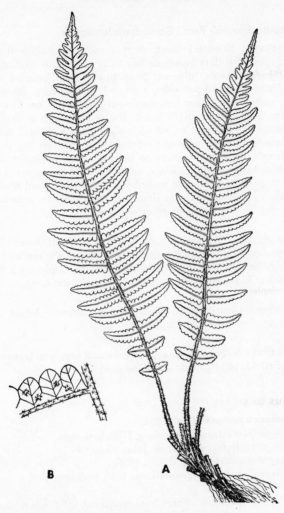

STIFF STAR-HAIR FERN : *Goniopteris sclerophylla*

A. Plant, reduced. B. Segments.

Free-tip Star-hair Fern : *Goniópteris tetrágona*

FEATURES: Rootstock stout, short-creeping at shallow depth, tipped with dark-brown stellate-hairy scales and sending up clustered fronds. Stipe *ca.* 20 to 40 cm. long, 4-angled with shallowly channeled sides, pale and stellate-hairy. Blade of a unique olive-green hue, somewhat translucent, *ca.* 20 to 40 cm. long and 15 to 30 broad, few pinnate with a terminal pinna-like segment set off on a distinct stalk. Pinnae rather broad, although narrower on the fertile than on the sterile fronds, cut about midway to the prominent fine-hairy midvein. Lobes broad, close-set, entire, acutish, fine-ciliate. Lowest and sometimes also second vein-pair uniting and sending up a compound vein to sinus-base. Sori close-set near midvein. Indusia fragmentary or obsolete.

RANGE: Fla., Hernando Co. to Marion Co. [Trop. Amer.] The restricted range here is inferred to be due to the species having been brought to this country from the tropics by a hurricane in relatively recent time, in the geologic sense.

HABITAT: Damp woods, often around limestone ledges and sinks. Soil circumneutral.

CULTURE: Sufficiently unusual in color and aspect to be worthy of trial in mild-climate woodland gardens.

NOMENCLATURE:

Goniopteris tetragona Presl, 1836.
(*Polypodium tetragonum* Swartz, 1788, basionym.)
Thelypteris tetragona E. P. St. John, 1936. (S)
Dryopteris subtetragona Maxon, 1926.
(*Polypodium subtetragonum* Link, 1833, basionym.)

For this taxon the epithet *tetragona* is not valid, when placed in the genus *Dryopteris,* in which case *subtetragona* must be used instead. All modern workers agree, however, that it belongs to a genus only remotely related to that (though they differ as to whether this should be *Goniopteris* or *Thelypteris*), so *tetragona* is usable after all.

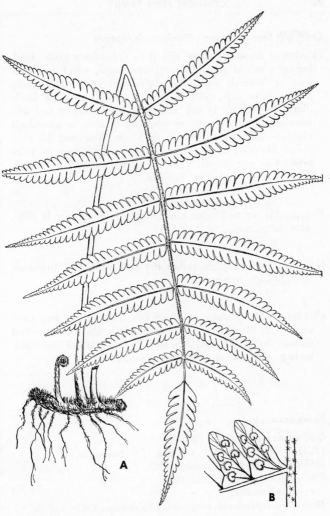

FREE-TIP STAR-HAIR FERN : *Goniopteris tetragona*

A. Plant, reduced. B. Segments.

Creeping Star-hair Fern : *Goniópteris réptans*

FEATURES: Rootstock short, tipped by pale-brown scales, sending up a tuft of arching to reclining fronds, which may take
root at intervals when the rachis and tip contact damp
humus. Stipe pale, stellate-hairy, *ca.* 5 to 10 cm. long. Blade
markedly variable in size and shape, from oblong and uniformly pinnate without any tendency to root, to irregularly
elongate and rooting, *ca.* 15 to 30 cm. long and 2.5 to 5
broad. Hairs on upper surface mostly stellate, those on veins
beneath in part simple. Veins inconspicuous. Sori few, small,
near midvein. Indusium vestigial.

RANGE: Fla. up to Marion and Levy cos.; found here in 1883.
[Caribbean lands.]

HABITAT: On seemingly rather dry sink walls and limestone
cliffs. Soil circumneutral.

CULTURE: The manner in which this fern spreads into mats
suggests its use as a rock-garden subject in Fla. It has proved
difficult to get started, however, unless most of the older
herbage is removed when transplanting.

NOMENCLATURE:

Goniopteris reptans Presl, 1836. (S)
(*Polypodium reptans* J. F. Gmelin, 1791, basionym.)
Dryopteris reptans Christensen, 1905.
Thelypteris reptans Morton, 1951.
    FLORIDA VARIANT:
Dryopteris reptans var. *conformis* Christensen, 1905.

This varietal name was based on the supposed tendency of
the Fla. plants to have more frequent relatively large uniform
fronds than those in the W.I., but in view of the marked variability in both areas, it is not considered worthy of acceptance.

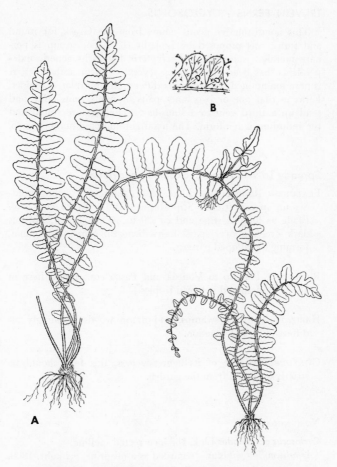

CREEPING STAR-HAIR FERN : *Goniopteris reptans*

A. Plant, reduced.   B. Section of a pinna.

TRI-VEIN FERNS : CYCLOSÒRUS

This nondistinctive genus name, from the Greek for round and sorus, was proposed by Link in 1833. The group is perhaps merely a subgenus of *Thelypteris,* but as its generic independence has been accepted by several eminent authorities, it is here maintained. Its members differ from the related Maiden Ferns in that one or two inner pairs of pinna-veins unite and send up a third vein to a sinus-base. The sori are round and the indusium is reniform. The basal chromosome number is 36.

Spready Tri-vein Fern : *Cyclosòrus gongylòdes*

FEATURES: Rootstock cord-like, black, glabrous, creeping, sending up spaced fronds. Stipe brown, *ca.* 38 to 75 cm. long. Blade as long as stipe and *ca.* 20 to 40 cm. broad, lustrous dark green above, sparse-hairy beneath. Sori submarginal, forming a scalloped pattern.

RANGE: S. Fla. up to Volusia and Pasco cos.; found here in 1877. [Widespread in world tropics.]

HABITAT: Marshes, swamps, and damp woods, seemingly indifferent to soil reaction.

CULTURE: Because of its aggressiveness, this fern should be strictly excluded from the garden.

NOMENCLATURE:

Cyclosorus gongylodes Link, 1833, corrected spelling.
(*Aspidium "goggilodus"* [regarded as a misprint] Schkuhr, 1809, basionym.)
Dryopteris gongylodes Kuntze, 1891.
Thelypteris gongylodes Small, 1938. (S)

Several other combinations have been proposed, but are rarely used. The epithet *unitum* (Linnaeus, 1759) has also been mistakenly applied to this fern.

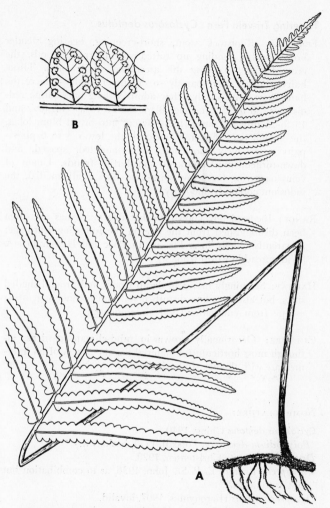

SPREADY TRI-VEIN FERN : *Cyclosorus gongylodes*
A. Plant, reduced. B. Segments.

Tapering Tri-vein Fern : *Cyclosòrus dentàtus*

FEATURES: Rootstock stout, short-creeping, bearing slender brown scales, sending up tufted subdimorphic fronds, the erect fertile exceeding the ascending sterile ones. Tissue hairy, though only sparsely so on upper blade surface, the hairs short, with rarely a few admixed long ones. Stipe reddish, *ca.* 38 to 75 cm. long. Blade *ca.* 38 to 75 cm. long and 13 to 25 broad. Pinnae shallowly cut into broad blunt lobes, the medial ones obscurely auricled, the lower 3 to 6 pinna-pairs successively shortened, longer-auricled, spaced, and down-turned, most markedly on fertile fronds. Union of veins occurring far below sinus-base. Sori small, medial, the indusium copiously fine-hairy.

RANGE: Incompletely known, in that this taxon has not often been distinguished from the one on the following text-page; apparently chiefly in s. Fla. up to Polk and Hernando cos. [Widespread in world tropics.]

HABITAT: Seemingly native in damp woods and around shaded sinks, but also invading disturbed soil in a manner suggesting escape from cultivation. Soil circumneutral.

CULTURE: Occasionally grown in mild-climate gardens, although most horticultural material has the aspect of an intermediate with the next-following taxon.

NOMENCLATURE:

Cyclosorus dentatus Ching, 1940.
(*Polypodium dentatum* Forskål, 1775, basionym.)
Dryopteris dentata Christensen, 1920.
Thelypteris dentata E. P. St. John, 1936, as to combination but not as to taxon.
Dryopteris mollis Hieronymus, 1907, invalid.
(*Polypodium molle* Jacquin, 1789, basionym.)
Thelypteris reducta Small, 1938. (S) (The combination *Thelypteris dentata* was applied by Small to the next-following taxon; this nomenclatorial mixup is discussed on the following text-page).

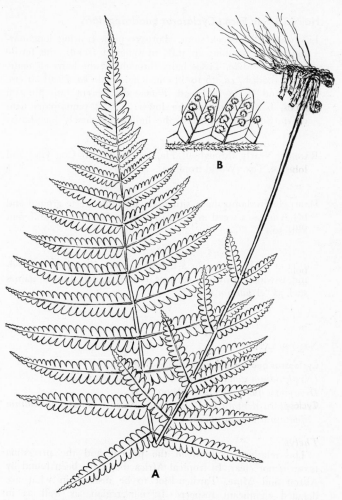

TAPERING TRI-VEIN FERN : *Cyclosorus dentatus*

A. Plant, reduced. B. Segments.

EBM

Hairy Tri-vein Fern : *Cyclosòrus quadrangulàris*

FEATURES: Rootstock stout, short-creeping, bearing long narrow scales, sending up tufts of suberect fronds, the fertile
and sterile alike. Tissue hairy throughout, the hairs elongate.
Stipe reddish, *ca.* 15 to 30 cm. long. Blade *ca.* 25 to 50 cm.
long and 10 to 20 broad. Pinnae deeply cut into bluntish
lobes, barely auricled, the lower 1 or 2 pinna-pairs bent
down. Sori small, medial, the indusium sparsely long-hairy.

RANGE: Nearly throughout Fla., up to Terrell Co., Ga., and
out to e. Tex. [World tropics.]

HABITAT: In damp shady situations, invading waste ground and
behaving as a weed in cultivated areas. Seemingly indifferent
as to soil.

CULTURE: This taxon, or a hybrid between it and the preceding, is widely grown in gardens, usually under obsolete names
such as *"Aspidium molle."*

NOMENCLATURE:

Cyclosorus quadrangularis Tardieu-Blot, 1952.
(*Nephrodium quadrangulare* Fée, 1852, basionym.)
Dryopteris quadrangularis Alston, 1937.
Thelypteris dentata E. P. St. John, 1936 (S); not *Polypodium
dentatum* Forskål, 1775.

The relationship between the present and the preceding
taxon is not clear. In tropical Africa they have been found by
Alston and Mme. Tardieu-Blot to be distinct in what are
deemed significant respects. In our region, as well as in
Jamaica, however, intermediates between them are frequent;
this could of course be due to hybridization, but that explana-
tion is disfavored by the manner in which the forms grown in
southern gardens (and northern greenhouses) spread copiously
by spores. Further investigation is manifestly needed.

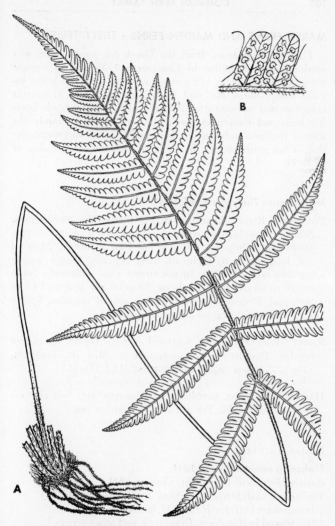

BROAD TRI-VEIN FERN : *Cyclosorus quadrangularis*

A. Frond, reduced. B. Segments.

MARSH FERNS AND MAIDEN FERNS : *THELÝPTERIS*

This technical term, from the Greek for female fern, was used as a species epithet by Linnaeus in 1753, and as a genus name by Schmidel in 1762; some workers hold the latter invalid under the Code, and favor *Lastrea*. Genus characters comprise two vascular strands in the stipe, pinnate blade bearing hairs and sometimes also scales, and delicate (rarely obsolete) reniform indusium. It is separable into two groups; the first, *Thelypteris* proper, has a basal chromosome number of 27 to 35.

Marsh Fern : *Thelýpteris palústris*

FEATURES: Rootstock nearly smooth. Blade thin, bluish-green. Sori partly hidden by reflexed margins. In WIDESPREAD VAR. (*pubéscens*): Stipe *ca.* 25 to 50 cm. long. Blade *ca.* 20 to 40 cm. long and 8 to 15 broad, hairy beneath. Pinnae deeply cut into bluntish lobes. In SOUTHERN VAR. (*haleàna*): Stipe *ca.* 30 to 60 cm. long. Blade *ca.* 30 to 60 cm. long and 10 to 20 broad. Pinnae cut into somewhat spaced pinnules. Sparse scales present on rachis and pinna-midrib.

RANGE: WIDESPREAD VAR., scattered over our region, commoner northw. SOUTHERN VAR., common in Miss. R. lowlands, rare e. over our region and northw. [Old World.]

HABITAT: Meadows, marshes, moist barrens, etc. Soil circumneutral to subacid. Too spready for garden use.

NOMENCLATURE:

Thelypteris palustris Schott, 1834.
Lastrea thelypteris Bory de St. Vincent, 1824.
Thelypteris thelypteris Nieuwland, 1910, inacceptable. (S)
(*Acrostichum thelypteris* L., 1753, basionym.)
(Also placed in *Aspidium, Dryopteris,* and other genera.)
  VARIETIES:
Thelypteris palustris var. *pubescens* Fernald, 1929.
(*Lastrea thelypteris* α *pubescens* Lawson, 1864, basionym.)
Thelypteris palustris var. *haleana* Fernald, 1929.

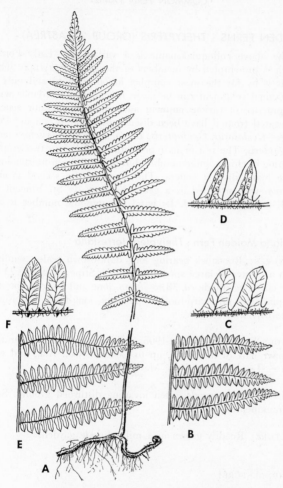

MARSH FERN : *Thelypteris palustris*

Widespread variety: A. Plant, reduced. B. Pinnae.
C. Sterile and D. Fertile segments.
Southern variety: E. Pinnae. F. Pinnules.

MAIDEN FERNS : THELÝPTERIS (GROUP 2, LASTRÈA)

The above colloquial name is a variant of "Lady Fern," which is pre-empted by members of the genus *Athyrium*. This genus is by far the most complex in our region, and only a provisional treatment can be given herein. In accordance with the practice of various eminent authorities, five minor genera segregated from it have been discussed separately, on previous pages—*Cyclosorus, Goniopteris, Leptogramma, Meniscium,* and *Phegopteris.* The rest of its representatives fall into two groups differing in chromosome number, but too slightly in morphology to be made distinct genera. The name of the second group, *Lastrea,* was proposed as a genus by Bory de St. Vincent in 1824, to honor a friend. Its basal chromosome number is 36.

Mariana Maiden Fern : Thelýpteris torresiàna

FEATURES: Rootstock bearing long dark-brown scales, sending up a cluster of large spreading fronds. Stipe stout, *ca.* 25 to 50 cm. long. Blade *ca.* 38 to 75 cm. long and 25 to 50 broad, 2-pinnate with sharp-toothed pinnules, long-hairy. Indusium short-lived or obsolete.

RANGE: Found in Fla. in 1906, and by now spread over the upper part of that state, up to Conecuh Co., Ala., and out to e. Tex. [Native of the Mariana Islands.]

HABITAT: Moist woods, often invading disturbed ground. Soil circumneutral to subacid.

CULTURE: Readily grown in a mild-climate garden.

NOMENCLATURE:

Thelypteris torresiana Alston, 1960.
(*Polystichum torresianum* Gaudichaud, 1828, basionym.)
Lastrea torresiana Moore, 1856.
Dryopteris setigera Kuntze, 1891, misapplied here. (S)
(*Cheilanthes setigera* Blume, 1828, basionym.)
Dryopteris uliginosa Christensen, 1934, preoccupied.
(*Aspidium uliginosum* Kunze, 1847, basionym.)

MARIANA MAIDEN FERN : *Thelypteris torresiana*

A. Portions of plant, reduced.   B. Segment.

Wax-dot Maiden Fern : *Thelýpteris resinifera*

FEATURES: Rootstock stout, erect, sending up a tuft of large plume-like fronds. Stipe *ca.* 8 to 15 cm. long, scaly below. Blade *ca.* 60 to 120 cm. long and 13 to 25 broad, some pinnae bearing a conspicuous wax-gland. Medial pinnae numerous, close-set, broad-based and tapering to acuminate tip; lower ones wide-spaced and successively shorter until the last are mere wings. Segments obliquely acutish, revolute-margined, the basal ones forming auricles. Sori few, spaced, small; indusium short-lived.

RANGE: Fla., in a small area in Pasco and Polk cos.; found here in 1881. [Widespread in trop. Amer.]

HABITAT: Swamps and damp woods; soil subacid.

CULTURE: Ornamental and worthy of trial in a mild-climate woodland garden.

NOMENCLATURE:

Thelypteris resinifera Proctor, 1953.
(*Polypodium resiniferum* Desvaux, 1811, basionym.)
Dryopteris resinifera Weatherby, 1936.
Lastrea resinifera Copeland, 1947.
Dryopteris panamensis Christensen, 1907.
(*Nephrodium panamense* Presl, 1825, basionym.)
Thelypteris panamensis E. P. St. John, 1936. (S)

This tropical taxon resembles in the down-tapering blade the temperate Tapering or New York Fern, *T. noveboracensis,* but they are only remotely related, having markedly different chromosome numbers. Another tropical one, here classed as *Cyclosorus dentatus,* also tapers, but its veining is different.

The present one has been assigned at least a dozen name combinations besides those listed, but none of them are in current use.

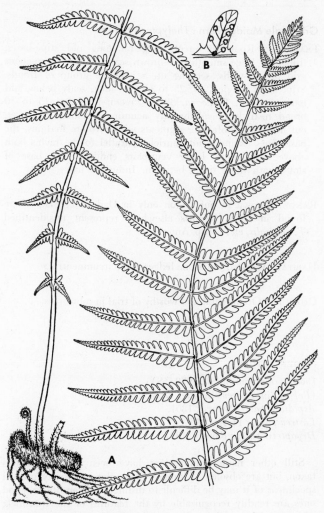

WAX-DOT MAIDEN FERN : *Thelypteris resinifera*
A. Plant, reduced. B. Segment.

Grid-scale Maiden Fern : *Thelýpteris pàtens*

FEATURES: Rootstock erect, long retaining old stipe-bases, tipped by large smooth pale-brown scales with a conspicuous grid of cell-walls, sending up a vase-like group of fronds. Stipe stout, angled, *ca.* 25 to 50 cm. long, scaly below and hairy upward. Blade *ca.* 38 to 75 cm. long and 15 to 30 broad near base, subabruptly acuminate. Pinnae close-set, cut into long subfalcate segments with revolute margins, the basal ones extended into auricles parallel to the rachis both above and below. Inner vein-pairs ending above base of sinus, with thick tissue between. Indusium hairy.

RANGE: Known in our region only in Dade Co., Fla., where found in 1905. Reports elsewhere represent misidentified *T. normalis,* etc. [Trop. Amer.]

HABITAT: Wooded limestone ledges. Soil circumneutral.

CULTURE: Ornamental and worthy of trial in subtropics.

NOMENCLATURE:

Thelypteris patens Small, 1938. (S)
(*Polypodium patens* Swartz, 1788, basionym.)
Aspidium patens Swartz, 1801.
Lastrea patens Presl, 1836.
Dryopteris patens Kuntze, 1891.

Still other name-combinations have been applied to this taxon, but are obsolete. Although incomplete or poorly pressed specimens of it may be difficult to distinguish from others, good ones are readily recognizable by the features of the rootstock, scales, auricles, and basal veins. Many specimens in herbaria labeled as taxon *patens* are misidentified. The *"Aspidium patens"* figured in Eaton's *Ferns of North America,* Vol. 2, pl. 70, 1880, comprises both *T. normalis* and *T.* × *versicolor,* treated below.

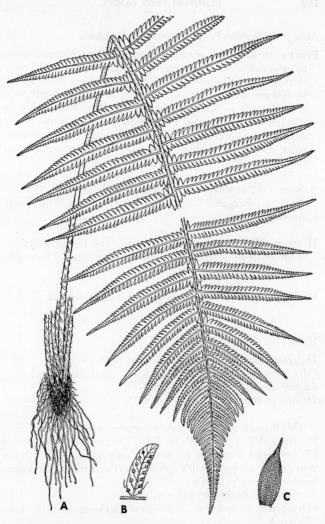

GRID-SCALE MAIDEN FERN : *Thelypteris patens*

A. Plant, reduced.   B. Segment.   C. Scale, enlarged.

Abrupt-tip Maiden Fern : *Thelýpteris augéscens*

FEATURES: Rootstock woody, tipped with long narrow brown hairy scales, sending up large spreading firm-textured fronds in two rows. Stipe stout, *ca.* 25 to 50 cm. long. Blade *ca.* 50 to 100 cm. long and 25 to 50 broad at base, abruptly contracted at tip to a long lobed segment, the rachis and midribs bearing hairy scales. Pinnae only *ca.* 1 cm. wide, barely auricled, the lower narrow-based; segments acute. Inner veinpairs ending in thickish tissue near sinus-base. Indusium bristly.

RANGE: Fla., in three disjunct areas: Dade–Osceola, Marion–Alachua–Dixie, and Liberty cos.; found here in 1915. [Trop. Amer.]

HABITAT: Various, thinly wooded slopes and limestone ledges, often invading quarry dumps and disturbed ground generally. Soil circumneutral.

CULTURE: Occasionally grown in mild-climate gardens.

NOMENCLATURE:

Thelýpteris augescens Munz & Johnston, 1922. (S)
(*Aspidium augescens* [Link, 1841] Kunze, 1851, basionym.)
Lastrea augescens John Smith, 1864.
Dryopteris augescens Christensen, 1913.

This taxon is markedly variable, intergrading southward with the tropical *T. serra* R. P. St. John, 1938, of which no typical Fla. material seems to be known, only intermediates being represented among Small's specimens. The variant developing northward may be known as:
Thelýpteris × *lindheìmeri* Wherry, p. 346.
(*Dryopteris normalis* v. *lindheimeri* Christensen, 1913, basionym.)
Thelypteris augescens lindheimeri R. P. St. John, 1938. (S)
This combines the characters of the present and next-following taxa, and as its spores are abortive, its hybrid origin is considered established.

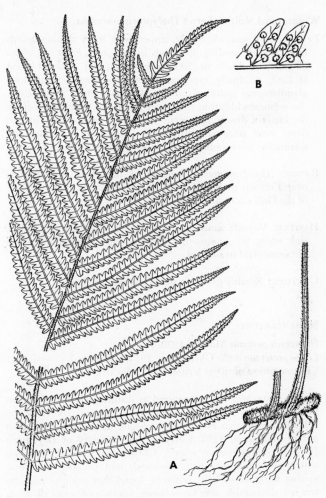

ABRUPT-TIP MAIDEN FERN : *Thelypteris augescens*

A. Portions of plant, reduced.   B. Segments.

Widespread Maiden Fern : *Thelýpteris normàlis*

FEATURES: Rootstock woody, tipped with hairy shining brown linear scales, sending up fronds in two rows. Stipe *ca.* 25 to 50 cm. long. Blade *ca.* 30 to 60 cm. long and 15 to 30 broad at base, gradually tapering upward, bearing beneath long glandless and sparse gland-tipped hairs. Pinnae subopposite, the segments bluntish, the upper basal one forming an erect, the lower a diverging auricle. Inner vein-pairs ending in thin tissue near sinus-base. Indusium long-hairy. Variable, and seemingly intergrading with various other Maiden Ferns.

RANGE: The commonest member of the genus in our area, over Fla., up to Berkeley Co., S.C., and through the s. half of the Gulf states to e. Tex. [W.I.]

HABITAT: Varied: moist to dryish woods, shaded rocky slopes, sink walls, etc., sometimes invading disturbed ground. Soil circumneutral to subacid.

CULTURE: Readily grown in shady lowland gardens.

NOMENCLATURE:

Thelypteris normalis Moxley, 1920. (S)
(*Dryopteris normalis* Christensen, 1910, basionym.)
(Taxon *patens* of many writers, not of Swartz, 1788.)

This taxon was first recognized as distinct, with emphasis on the double row of fronds along the horizontal rootstock, by Jenman in Jamaica in 1896; he mistook it, however, for taxon *patens* of Swartz, 1788. Carrying out his study of *Dryopteris* (in the comprehensive sense), Christensen realized that two widely different taxa were involved, and proposed the new epithet *normalis* in 1910. Then he found that the real problem was to distinguish the latter from taxon *augescens* of Link, 1841. A disconcerting number of specimens proved to combine their differentiating characters in complex pattern, and these he named var. *lindheimeri* in reference to an active collector of such material; that this should be treated as a hybrid is pointed out on the preceding text-page.

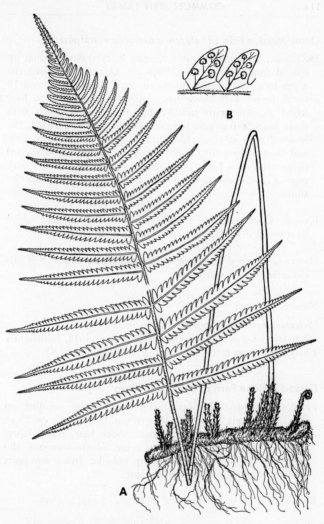

WIDESPREAD MAIDEN FERN : *Thelypteris normalis*

A. Plant, reduced.   B. Segments.

Ovate Maiden Fern : Thelýpteris normàlis v. hárperi

FEATURES: Rootstock slender, bearing hairy scales, sending up spaced fronds in one row. Stipe *ca.* 13 to 25 cm. long, its scales long and slender. Blade *ca.* 18 to 35 cm. long and 13 to 25 broad well above base, narrowed upward to a long lobed segment with tail-like tip, pubescent beneath with short hairs, a few gland-tipped. Pinnae barely auricled, the lower 2 or 3 successively shortened pairs narrowed to base and bent downward. Inner vein-pairs ending in thickened tissue near sinus base. Indusium fine-hairy. Intergrades with type *T. normalis* deemed too frequent to justify species status.

RANGE: Over much of Fla., up to Pulaski Co., Ga., where discovered in 1902, and out to Mobile Co., Ala.

HABITAT: Wooded limestone ledges and loamy slopes. Soil circumneutral. Not cultivated.

NOMENCLATURE:

Thelypteris normalis v. harperi Wherry, p. 346.
(*Dryopteris normalis* v. *harperi* Christensen, 1913, basionym.)
Thelypteris ovata & [v.] *harperi* R. P. St. John, 1938 (S)

Curved Maiden Fern : Thelýpteris "únca"

FEATURES: Rootstock tipped with ovate scales, sending up clustered fronds. Stipe *ca.* 20 to 40 cm. long. Blade *ca.* 25 to 50 cm. long and 10 to 20 broad above base, finely hairy. Pinnae curved, deeply cut into acute falcate segments, the lowest of which form auricles; tip tail-like. Inner vein-pairs ending in thin tissue near sinus-base.

RANGE: Fla. up to Alachua and Dixie cos.; found in 1934.

HABITAT: Open rocky woods. Soil circumneutral. Not cult'd.

NOMENCLATURE:

Thelypteris unca R. P. St. John, 1938. (S)

OVATE MAIDEN FERN : *Thelypteris normalis var. harperi*

A. Plant, reduced.   B. Segments.

Meager Maiden Fern : Thelýpteris "macilénta"

FEATURES: Rootstock short, tipped with long narrow glossy scales, sending up a sparse tuft of erect fronds. Stipe *ca.* 8 to 15 cm. long, fine-hairy. Blade *ca.* 15 to 30 cm. long and 3 to 6 broad below middle, with *ca.* 3 lower pinna-pairs successively shortened and bent downward, long-acuminate. Pinnae short, acutish. Lower of the inner vein-pairs ending at sinus-base, upper well up the side. Sori few, close to midrib; indusium sparse-hairy.

RANGE: Known only at one spot in Hernando Co., Fla., where discovered in 1934. Seemingly now extinct.

HABITAT: Wooded limestone ledges. Soil circumneutral. Not cultivated.

NOMENCLATURE:

Thelypteris macilenta E. P. St. John, 1936. (S)
Dryopteris macilenta Correll, 1938.

Trailing Maiden Fern : Thelýpteris "macrorhizòma"

FEATURES: Rootstock several hundred cm. long, retaining many old stipe-bases. Stipe *ca.* 10 to 20 cm. long, glabrous. Blade triangular, with long-acuminate tip ending in a tail-like segment, *ca.* 25 to 50 cm. long and 15 to 30 broad at base. Sori submarginal.

RANGE: Known only at "The Cove," in Citrus Co., Fla., where discovered in 1938.

HABITAT: Forming a low thicket in a swamp. Soil subacid. Not cultivated.

NOMENCLATURE:

Thelypteris macrorhizoma E. P. St. John, 1942.

The above two rare endemics are too little known for their relationships to have been established.

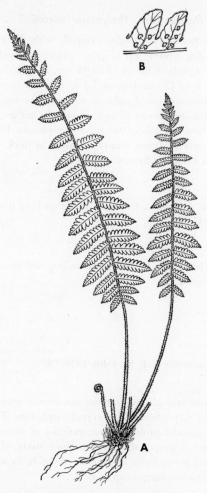

MEAGER MAIDEN FERN : *Thelypteris "macilenta"*
A. Plant, reduced.   B. Segments.

Blunt-pinna Maiden Fern : *Thelýpteris "saxátilis"*

FEATURES: Rootstock slender, tipped with long-triangular brown scales, sending up a sparse cluster of small erect or ascending fronds. Stipe *ca.* 8 to 15 cm. long, hairy upward. Blade *ca.* 8 to 15 cm. long and 3 to 6 broad below middle, the long terminal lobed segment with tail-like tip, pubescent with long hairs. Pinnae of general elliptic outline, shallowly cut into broadish lobes, the tip a conspicuous bluntish triangular segment. Inner vein-pair ending in thick tissue near sinus-base. Indusium firm, short-hairy.   .

RANGE: Fla., Columbia Co. to Washington Co.; discovered in Hamilton Co. in 1934.

HABITAT: Thinly wooded limestone ledges. Soil circumneutral. Not cultivated.

NOMENCLATURE:

Thelypteris saxatilis R. P. St. John, 1938. (S)

Although in typical development the several preceding taxa look distinct, they seemingly intergrade with type *T. normalis,* so are here deemed probably mere varieties of that; no formal status change is proposed, however, since study of the intermediates may prove them to represent hybrids, in which event appropriate name-changes can be made.

In the case of the next-following taxon, on the other hand, apparent intermediates with *T. normalis* give every indication of hybrid origin, so independence is accepted. Further study of the whole series of taxa is manifestly needed.

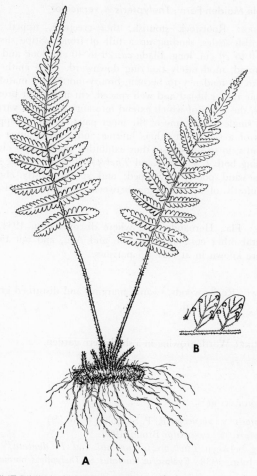

BLUNT-PINNA MAIDEN FERN : *Thelypteris "saxatilis"*

A. Plant, reduced.   B. Segments.

Variable Maiden Fern : *Thelýpteris* × *versicolor*

FEATURES: Rootstock stoutish, short-creeping, tipped with brownish scales, sending up a tuft of fronds. Stipe slender, *ca.* 10 to 20 cm. long. Blade *ca.* 20 to 40 cm. long and 8 to 15 broad, moderately tapering downward. (The epithet refers to its tendency to become bronzy-mottled at maturity.) Pinnae rather broad and well spaced, cut into blunt broadish lobes, the lower of which extend into auricles. Veins variable, on a single blade some of the inner pairs ending on opposite sides of a sinus, but others uniting and sending up a compound vein to sinus-base, thus exhibiting the features characterizing both *Cyclosorus* and *Thelypteris*. Sori tending to be sparse and poorly developed, and spores mostly aborted. Manifestly of hybrid origin between distantly related taxa.

RANGE: Fla., Hernando Co., where discovered in 1934, and several other cos., up to c. Ga. and Ala., and out to La., where known in at least 15 parishes.

HABITAT: Rocky woods, swamp margins, and disturbed ground. Soil circumneutral.

CULTURE: Worth growing in a shady fern garden.

NOMENCLATURE:

Thelypteris [×] *versicolor* R. P. St. John, 1938. (S)
Dryopteris [×] *versicolor* Broun, 1938.
"Lying between *Thelypteris normalis* and *T. dentata*," R. P. St. John, 1938: *Cyclosorus dentatus* × *Thelypteris normalis.*

The ability of the last-named pair of taxa to hybridize is admittedly an argument against separating them generically, although crosses between members of other assumedly distinct genera are not unknown. At any rate this hybrid tends to develop wherever the indicated parents grow together.

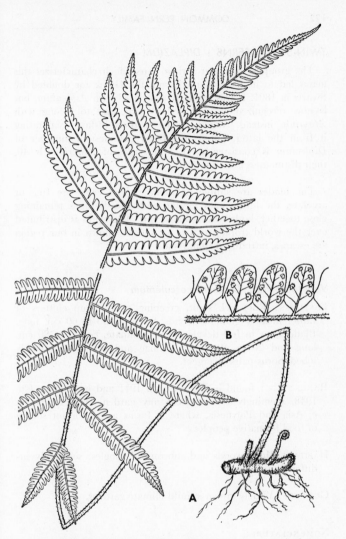

VARIABLE MAIDEN FERN : *Thelypteris* × *versicolor*
A. Plant, reduced. B. Segments, showing variable veins.

TWIN-SORUS FERNS : *DIPLÀZIUM*

The grouping of linear sori in pairs which characterizes this genus led to its being named from the Greek for doubled by Swartz in 1801. It was formerly associated with *Asplenium,* but is now recognized as unrelated to that, and to belong with *Athyrium* instead. Actually some workers disfavor separating it from the latter, but as the basal chromosome number of *Diplazium* is consistently 41, while that of *Athyrium* is 40, their distinctness is maintained.

The blades are simple or pinnate. The veins are free or areolate, the fertile ones forking with the divisions remaining close together, both bearing linear sori. The genus is distributed over the world tropics; two of its species known in our region are escapes, introduced from Asia.

Vegetable Fern : *Diplàzium esculéntum*

FEATURES: Rootstock stout, creeping, sending up clusters of rather massive glabrous fronds. Stipe *ca.* 30 to 60 cm. long. Blade 1- or in full development 2-pinnate, *ca.* 40 to 80 cm. long and 20 to 40 broad. Pinnae and pinnules shallowly lobed. Sorus-pairs divergent.

RANGE: Fla.: found in Dade Co. in 1941 and in De Soto Co. 1948, seemingly remote from any garden. [Widespread in e. Asia and Polynesia, where it forms an important source of food for native peoples.]

HABITAT: Moist woods and subtropical jungles; seemingly in-different as to soil.

CULTURE: Widely grown in mild-climate gardens.

NOMENCLATURE:

Diplazium esculentum Swartz, 1803.
(*Hemionitis esculenta* Retzius, 1791, basionym.)
Asplenium esculentum Presl, 1825.
Athyrium esculentum Copeland, 1940.

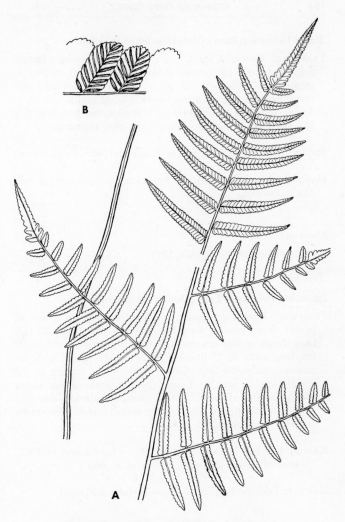

VEGETABLE FERN : *Diplazium esculentum*

A. Portions of frond, reduced.   B. Segments.

Broad Twin-sorus Fern : *Diplàzium lonchophýllum*

FEATURES: Rootstock stout, erect, sending up close-set fronds. Stipe bearing long narrow brown scales, *ca.* 10 to 20 cm. long. Blade firm-textured, ovate, gradually narrowed upward, glabrous except for somewhat scaly rachis, *ca.* 15 to 30 cm. long and 10 to 20 broad. Pinnae rather broad, deeply cut, the lobes fine-serrate toward tip. Sori scattered.

RANGE: La., Iberia Par., where found in 1938. [Trop. Amer.]

HABITAT: Wooded slopes, in humus-rich circumneutral soil. Not cultivated.

NOMENCLATURE:

Diplazium lonchophyllum Kunze, 1839.

Japanese Twin-sorus Fern : *Diplàzium japónicum*

FEATURES: Rootstock slender, creeping, sending up a row of fronds. Stipe bearing long brown scales, *ca.* 10 to 20 cm. long. Blade oblong-triangular, long-acuminate, *ca.* 10 to 20 cm. long and 6 to 12 broad. Rachis grooved above, with the grooves continuous into pinnae (a diagnostic feature of the genus *Lunathyrium* Koidzumi), bearing both narrow scales and gland-tipped hairs. Lower pinnae shallowly cut into oblique serrate-tipped lobes, upper undulate-serrate to entire. Sori sparse and scattered.

RANGE: Escaped in Gadsden Co., Fla., where found in 1957. (Source of spores unknown; native of e. Asia.)

HABITAT: Disturbed soil in woods; doubtfully cultivated.

NOMENCLATURE:

Diplazium japonicum Beddome, 1876.
(*Asplenium japonicum* Thunberg, 1784, basionym.)
Lunathyrium japonicum Kurata, 1961.

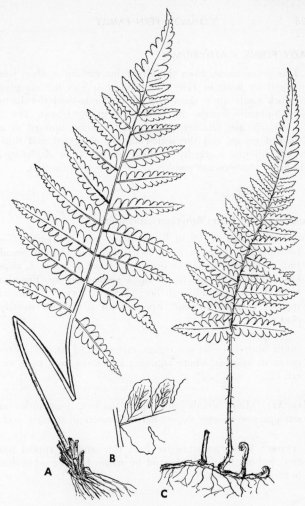

BROAD TWIN-SORUS FERN : *Diplazium lonchophyllum*

A. Plant, reduced. B. Segments.

JAPANESE TWIN-SORUS FERN : *Diplazium japonicum*

C. Plant, reduced.

LADY FERNS : *ATHÝRIUM*

This genus name, from the Greek for without a door, was proposed by Roth in 1799. In our few species the creeping rootstock sends up a short row of moderate-sized deciduous 1- to 2-pinnate fronds, the fertile late in the season. The 2 stipe-strands are flattened and curved, uniting upward to a U-shaped group, and the scale-cells are elongated and thin-walled, differing markedly in these respects from *Asplenium*. The basal chromosome number is 40, another distinction.

Southern Lady Fern : *Athýrium asplenioìdes*

FEATURES: Stipe *ca.* 20 to 40 cm. long, bearing fragile pale-brown scales. Blade *ca.* 25 to 50 cm. long and 15 to 30 broad just above base, or in the occasional NARROW FORM, f. *ellipticum,* only to 20 cm. broad *ca.* 3 pinna-pairs up. Pinnules toothed and short-auricled. Sori elongate, curved. Indusium sparsely glandular ciliate. Spores with a blackish wrinkly coat.

RANGE: Scattered over our region, rare south of lat. 30°. (Frequent in uplands, where attaining larger size, and n. to *ca.* lat. 42°.)

HABITAT: Moist woods and open thickets, hummocks in swamps, and springy slopes; soil moderately to strongly acid.

CULTURE: While an attractive fern, this tends to spread too rapidly both by rootstocks and by spores for safe admission to the small garden.

NOMENCLATURE:

Athyrium asplenioides A. Eaton, 1817. (S)
(*Nephrodium asplenioides* Michaux, 1803, basionym.)
A. filix-femina var. *asplenioides* Farwell, 1923.
    NARROW FORM:
A. asplenioides f. *ellipticum* Wherry, 1948.

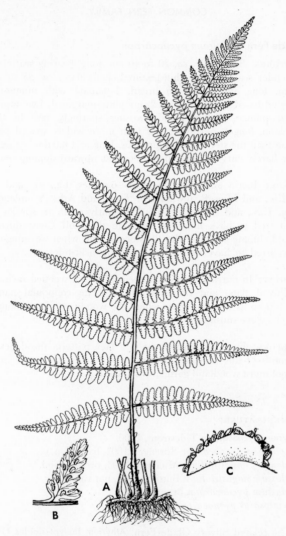

SOUTHERN LADY FERN : *Athyrium asplenioides*
A. Plant, reduced. B. Pinnule. C. Sorus, enlarged.

Glade Fern : *Athýrium pycnocárpon*

FEATURES: Stipe pale, *ca.* 20 to 40 cm. long, bearing scattered slender scales. Blade thin-textured, lanceolate, *ca.* 35 to 70 cm. long and 13 to 25 broad, 1-pinnate with numerous broad-based but not auricled, undulate-margined, long-tapering pinnae. Fertile fronds, arising sparingly late in the season, longer, narrower, and with more widely spaced pinnae than the sterile. Sori numerous, long and narrow, straight or barely curved, lying along close-set upward-sloping veins.

RANGE: Iberia and West Feliciana parishes, La., s.c. and n. Miss., and Miss. R. lowlands of Tenn. and Ark. (S. uplands, ne. U.S., and s. Can.) This dominantly northern species is inferred to have migrated south to the Gulf Coast during cold-climate stages of the Pleistocene, and when warming-up occurred to have developed moderate heat-tolerance.

HABITAT: In nutrient-rich circumneutral soil of wooded ravines, alluvial flats, and limestone slopes. The colloquial name refers to its favoring spots where the woods are open enough to let some sunshine in.

CULTURE: Even though not cut in a lacy pattern, the delicate fronds of this fern are so attractive as to make its use in a cool moist woodland garden worth while.

NOMENCLATURE:

Athyrium pycnocarpon Tidestrom, 1906.
(*Asplenium pycnocarpon* Sprengel, 1804, basionym.)
Asplenium angustifolium Michaux, 1803, preoccupied.
Diplazium angustifolium Butters, 1917, not valid.
Diplazium pycnocarpon Broun, 1938.
Homalosorus pycnocarpus Small, 1935. (S)

The related Silvery Glade Fern, *Athýrium thelypterioìdes* Desvaux, 1827, has much the same range as the above, but is rarer in our region, having been reported only from West Feliciana Par., La., and Obion Co., Tenn. It is discussed in *The Fern Guide*, p. 138, and in the Appendix.

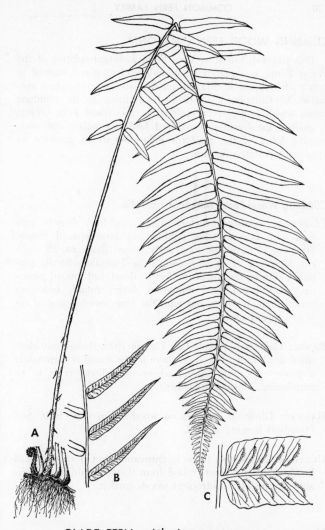

GLADE FERN : *Athyrium pycnocarpon*

A. Plant, reduced. B. Fertile pinnae.
C. Base of a fertile pinna, enlarged.

CLIMBING WOOD FERN : MAXÒNIA

This tropical-American Vine Fern, a distant relative of the Wood Ferns, was placed in an independent genus, named in honor of William R. Maxon, an eminent American fern specialist, by Christensen in 1916. In addition to the climbing habit, which is highly exceptional in the Wood Fern Group, it exhibits the features of reduced fertile pinnulets and over- lapping lobes of the reniform indusium, which produce an apparently peltate structure.

Climbing Wood Fern : *Maxònia apiifòlia*

FEATURES: Rootstock high-climbing, cord-like, densely cov- ered with brown scales, sending out large spaced fronds. Stipe *ca.* 15 to 30 cm. long, scaly below. Blade *ca.* 38 to 75 cm. long and 25 to 50 broad, 2- or 3-pinnate. Sterile pin- nulets elliptic, serrate, acute; fertile, developed toward pinna- tip, round-lobed. Sori numerous, large, round. Indusium conspicuous, reniform but with the lobes overlapping so far as to appear peltate.

RANGE: Collected in Dade Co., Fla., in 1921, though not iden- tified until 1961. The area where it was found is fortunately a protected private estate, where its rediscovery is to be anticipated. [Caribbean lands.]

HABITAT: Climbing on trees on wooded limestone hills. Soil (tree-bark humus) subacid.

CULTURE: Not known to be in cultivation, but if spores could be obtained and plants raised from them, should be a desir- able feature of a subtropical woods garden.

NOMENCLATURE:

Maxonia apiifolia Christensen, 1916.
(*Dicksonia apiifolia* Swartz, 1801, basionym.)
Dryopteris apiifolia Kuntze, 1891.

CLIMBING WOOD FERN : *Maxonia apiifolia*

A. Tip of rootstock and   B. Portion of blade, reduced.
C. Sterile and   D. Fertile portions.   E. Sori, enlarged.

131

NET-VEIN HOLLY FERNS : *CYRTÒMIUM*

Two new genera, *Cyrtomium* and *Phanerophlebia,* respectively from Greek words signifying cut in a curve and visible veins, were proposed by Presl in 1836. Most present-day workers consider these identical, in which case the former name is to be used, since it was the first to be applied to the species herein treated.

The firm texture, large scales, round sorus with peltate indusium, etc., indicate close relationship to the genus *Polystichum;* significant differences are the complexly reticulate veining and the scattering of the sori, some of which lie astride veins and others tip veinlets within areoles. One Asian species has escaped from cultivation in our region.

Asian Holly Fern : *Cyrtòmium falcàtum*

FEATURES: Rootstock short and stout, bearing conspicuous dark-brown scales. Fronds few, in a vase-like group. Stipe stout, *ca.* 10 to 20 cm. long, densely clothed with broad brown scales. Blade *ca.* 18 to 35 cm. long and 8 to 15 broad (much reduced in dry situations), leathery in texture, glossy dark green above. Pinnae few, large, close-set, obliquely ovate with curving acuminate tip.

RANGE: Escaped from cultivation at scattered points over our region; especially conspicuous at Ft. Marion, St. Augustine, Fla. [E. Asia.]

HABITAT: Invading masonry, heaps of rubble, and clayey banks; soil circumneutral.

CULTURE: Well known as a subject in mild-climate gardens, even being used locally as a ground-cover in woodland.

NOMENCLATURE:

Cyrtomium falcatum Presl, 1836.
(*Polypodium falcatum* L., jr., 1781, basionym.)
Phanerophlebia falcata Copeland, 1947, not valid.

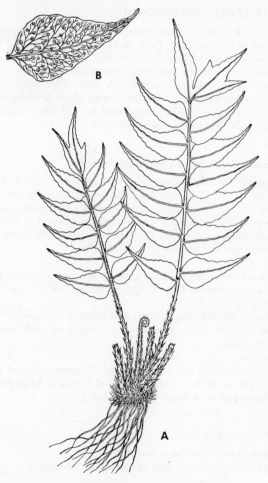

ASIAN HOLLY FERN : *Cyrtomium falcatum*

A. Plant, reduced. B. Pinna.

HOLLY FERNS : *POLÝSTICHUM*

A Greek term for many rows, in reference to the sori, was applied to this genus by Roth in 1799. Its members are moderate-sized, heavy-textured evergreens. The stout rootstock is copiously scaly at tip and retains many old stipe-bases, in the midst of which the clustered fronds arise. The stipe is short and scaly, with multiple vascular strands; blade 1- or 2-pinnate, with bristly margins. The round sori have a firm peltate indusium. The basal chromosome number is 41.

Christmas Fern : *Polýstichum acrostichoìdes*

FEATURES: Sterile fronds smaller than fertile, which have: Stipe *ca.* 10 to 20 cm. long. Blade *ca.* 25 to 50 cm. long and 6 to 12 broad. Pinnae oblong with conspicuous superior auricle, at or above mid-blade abruptly reduced in size, and fertile. The plate shows the common, type form along with several variants which occur sporadically.

RANGE: Over much of our region, though not extending south of mid-peninsular Fla. [S. upl., n. states, and se. Can.]

HABITAT: Shaded slopes and well-drained humus-rich flats. Soil subacid to circumneutral. Intolerant of high summer temperatures.

CULTURE: As this fern thrives in rather barren soils and tends to cover the surface with mats of old fronds, it helps prevent erosion and is of much garden value.

NOMENCLATURE:

Polystichum acrostichoides Schott, 1834. (S)
(*Nephrodium acrostichoìdes* Michaux, 1803, basionym.)

West Indies Holly Fern, *Polýstichum muricàtum* Fée, 1852, is bipinnate and resembles the Eastern Holly Fern (*The Fern Guide,* p. 98). It is grown to some extent in mild-climate gardens, and reported as an escape in s. Fla.

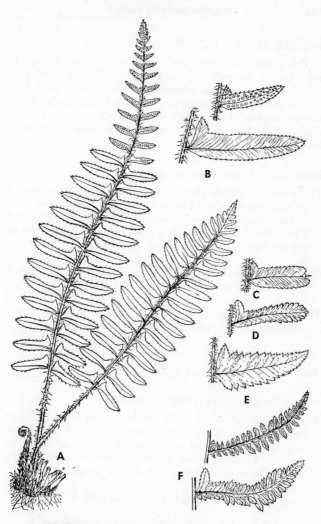

CHRISTMAS FERN : *Polystichum acrostichoides*

A. Plant, reduced.   Pinnae of forms: B. Type.
C. Bristled.   D. Frilled.   E. Incised.   F. Bipinnate.

HALBERD FERNS : *TECTÀRIA*

This genus name, from the latin word for roof, perhaps in reference to the way the fronds of some species overlap in shingle-like pattern, was proposed by Cavanilles in 1799. Our species are small rock-plants with more or less triangular, little-divided blades. The veins are conspicuously areolate. The indusium varies from peltate to reniform. The basal chromosome number is 40.

Least Halberd Fern : *Tectària mínima*

FEATURES: Rootstock slender, dark-scaly, sending up spaced arching fronds. Stipe *ca.* 8 to 15 cm. long, brown and scaly at base. Blade narrow-triangular, *ca.* 5 to 10 cm. long and 3 to 6 broad, lobed or with a basal pinna-pair. Veins forming few large areoles. Indusium reniform.

RANGE: Fla., Dade and Monroe cos. to Citrus Co.; discovered here in 1903. [Subsequently found in Cuba.]

HABITAT: Limestone ledges and sink walls, in rather sunny situations. Soil circumneutral. Not cultivated.

NOMENCLATURE:

Tectaria minima Underwood, 1906. (S)

Hybrid Halberd Fern : *Tectària* × *amesiàna*

FEATURES: Stipe *ca.* 13 to 25 cm. long, light brown, bearing scattered scales. Blade oblong-triangular, *ca.* 8 to 15 cm. long and 5 to 10 broad, with a spaced pinna-pair and lobed terminal segment. Veins forming numerous small areoles. Sori few, the spores aborted. Indusium reniform.

RANGE: Discovered in s. Dade Co., Fla., in 1903. Very rare.

HABITAT: Shaded sink walls. Soil circumneutral. Not cult'd.

NOMENCLATURE:

Tectaria [×] *amesiana* A. A. Eaton, 1906. (S)
T. coriandrifolia × *minima,* suggested by describer.

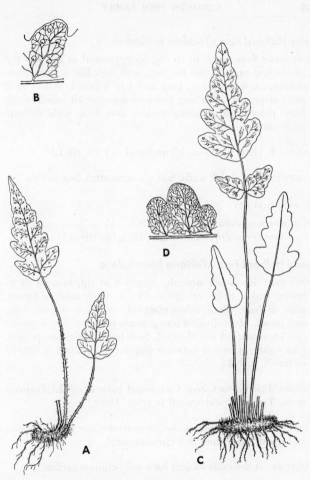

LEAST HALBERD FERN : *Tectaria minima*

A. Plant. B. Segment, enlarged.

HYBRID HALBERD FERN : *Tectaria × amesiana*

C. Plant. D. Segment, enlarged.

137

Hairy Halberd Fern : *Tectària coriandrifòlia*

FEATURES: Stipe *ca.* 5 to 10 cm. long, covered as are also the rachis and major veins beneath, with hair-like scales. Blade oblong, *ca.* 8 to 15 cm. long and 4 to 8 broad, with 1 or 2 pairs of pinnae and a long terminal segment, all round-lobed. New plants arising along rachis. Sori few, with delicate reniform indusium.

RANGE: S. Dade Co., Fla., where found in 1903. [W.I.]

HABITAT: Shaded sink walls. Soil circumneutral. Not cult'd.

NOMENCLATURE:

Tectaria coriandrifolia Underwood, 1906. (S)
(*Aspidium coriandrifolium* Swartz, 1801, basionym.)

Broad Halberd Fern : *Tectària heracleifòlia*

FEATURES: Rootstock stoutish, upturned at tip, bearing dark-brown scales. Stipe *ca.* 20 to 40 cm. long, reddish brown, scaly at base. Blade sub-pentagonal, *ca.* 15 to 30 cm. long and broad, often divided into a pinna-pair and 3 to 5 pinna-like segments; all round-lobed. Sori large. Indusium peltate. (An apparent hybrid between this and *T. minima* is figured by Small, p. 208.)

RANGE: Fla. up to Citrus Co.; found here in 1881. [Disjunct in w. Tex., and widespread in trop. Amer.]

HABITAT: Shaded limestone ledges, surroundings of small sinks, and woodland humus. Soil circumneutral.

CULTURE: A desirable subject for a mild-climate garden.

NOMENCLATURE:

Tectaria heracleifolia Underwood, 1906. (S)
(*Aspidium heracleifolium* Willdenow, 1810, basionym.)

A similar species, *T. cicutària* Copeland, 1907, was found as an escape in e. Dade Co., Fla., in 1911. It differs in the blade being narrower and bearing buds medially.

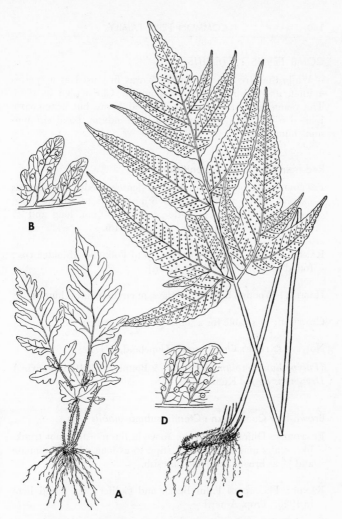

HAIRY HALBERD FERN : *Tectaria coriandrifolia*

A. Plant.   B. Segment, enlarged.

BROAD HALBERD FERN : *Tectaria heracleifolia*

C. Plant.   D. Segment, enlarged.

139

COMB FERNS : *CTENÌTIS*

While the Greek word for comb was first used as a species epithet, it was applied to this genus by Christensen in 1938. The plants suggest thin-textured Wood Ferns, but bear coarse jointed scales and hairs, and short-lived indusia. Basal chromosome number is 41.

Red-hair Comb Fern : *Ctenìtis ámpla*

FEATURES: Rootstock trunk-like, densely red-scaly. Fronds massive, in a vase-like group. Stipe *ca.* 35 to 70 cm. long, bearing slender scales. Blade *ca.* 40 to 80 cm. long and 25 to 50 broad, *ca.* 2-pinnate, hairy beneath.

RANGE: S. Fla., increasingly rare up to Polk and Manatee cos.; found here in 1903. [Trop. Amer.]

HABITAT: Wooded limestone ledges, in circumneutral humus.

CULTURE: Desirable for a subtropical fern garden.

NOMENCLATURE: *Ctenitis ampla* Copeland, 1947.

(*Polypodium amplum* Humboldt & Bonpland, 1810, basionym.)
Dryopteris ampla Kuntze, 1891. (S)

Brown-hair Comb Fern : *Ctenìtis submarginàlis*

FEATURES: Differing from the above in the rootstock not trunk-like, scales and hairs brown, stipe ½ as long, blade 1-pinnate and ½ as broad, and lobes obtusish.

RANGE: Fla. up to Palm Beach and Collier cos.; found here in 1926. [Trop. Amer.]

HABITAT: Circumneutral woods and swamps. Not cultivated.

NOMENCLATURE: *Ctenitis submarginalis* Copeland, 1947.

(*Polypodium submarginale* Langsdorf & Fischer, 1810, bas.)
Dryopteris submarginalis Christensen, 1905.
Thelypteris submarginalis Small, 1938. (S)

RED-HAIR COMB FERN : *Ctenitis ampla*

A. Plant, much-reduced.   B. Pinnule, enlarged.

BROWN-HAIR COMB FERN : *C. submarginalis*   C. Pinna.

WOOD FERNS : *DRYÓPTERIS*

The term dryopteris, from the Greek for oak fern, used by Linnaeus only as a species epithet, was made a genus name by Adanson in 1763, and defined, in the sense now accepted, by Schott in 1834. Numerous taxa once placed in the genus have been shifted to others, but it is still a large group, although only poorly represented in our region.

The rootstock is stout and scaly, long retaining old stipe bases. The clustered fronds are firm-textured. The scaly stipe encloses multiple strands, and the blade is moderately large and 1- or 2-pinnate. Round sori with a firm reniform indusium are borne astride vein branches. The basal chromosome number is 41.

Florida Wood Fern : *Dryópteris ludoviciàna*

FEATURES: Stipe *ca.* 15 to 30 cm. long. Blade lustrous dark green, *ca.* 50 to 100 cm. long and 15 to 30 broad. Terminal fertile divisions markedly contracted.

RANGE: Highlands Co., Fla., up to Columbus Co., N.C., and out to E. Baton Rouge Par., La., where found in the early 1800s. Frequent in Fla., but scattered elsewhere.

HABITAT: Swamps and damp woods; soil moderately acid.

CULTURE: Readily grown in a woodland garden and ornamental. Winter-hardy well north of our region.

NOMENCLATURE:

Dryopteris ludoviciana Small, 1938. (S)
(*Aspidium ludovicianum* Kunze, 1848, basionym.)
Nephrodium floridanum Hooker, 1850.
Dryopteris floridana Kuntze, 1891.

The epithet *ludoviciana* commemorates the state where discovered, traditionally by an otherwise unknown naturalist named Ludwig, who died from a snake bite.

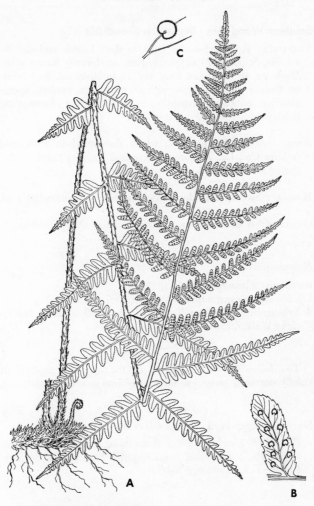

FLORIDA WOOD FERN : *Dryopteris ludoviciana*

A. Plant, reduced. B. Fertile pinnule.
C. Sorus, enlarged.

Southern Wood Fern : *Dryópteris* × *austràlis*

FEATURES: Rootstock-scales light to dark brown and dull to shining. Stipe *ca.* 20 to 40 cm. long, moderately brown scaly. Blade *ca.* 40 to 80 cm. long and 15 to 30 broad. Sori borne on slightly reduced upper pinnae, mostly *ca.* medial. Spores abortive, indicating hybridity, as does also the chromosome behavior.

RANGE: Ala., Cherokee Co., where discovered in 1936, and Auburn Co.; La., E. Baton Rouge and Rapides parishes. Reported without good evidence elsewhere.

HABITAT: Swamps and damp rocky woods; soil somewhat acid.

CULTURE: A striking fern, worthy of use in shady gardens.

NOMENCLATURE:

Dryopteris [×] *australis* Small, 1938. (S)
(*D. clintoniana* var. *australis* Wherry, 1937, basionym.)
A hybrid, Brown & Correll, 1942. Probably *D. celsa* × *ludoviciana* Walker, 1961.

The following two members of the genus *Dryopteris* of chiefly northern range extend locally into our region:

Narrow Swamp Fern : *Dryópteris cristàta* Gray, 1848.

(*The Fern Guide,* p. 106.) Resembling a narrowed form of any of the 3 preceding taxa. Rapides Par., La., to se. Ark. and ne. Tex. In swampy habitats.

Marginal Wood Fern : *Dryópteris marginàlis* Gray, 1848.

(*The Fern Guide,* p. 116.) Distinguished by its leathery texture and rounded segments, with sori lying close to margins. Reported at one station each in northernmost Ala. and Miss. In rocky habitats. See Appendix.

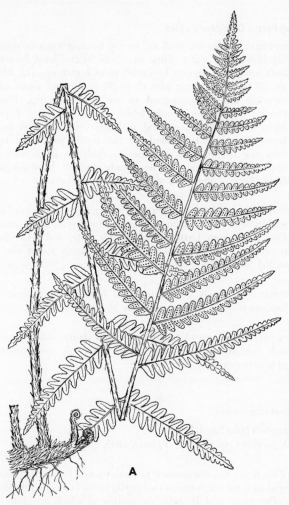

SOUTHERN WOOD FERN : *Dryopteris* × *australis*

A. Plant, reduced.

Log Fern : *Dryópteris célsa*

FEATURES: Rootstock shallow, its tip bearing copious shining
blackish-brown scales. Stipe *ca.* 25 to 50 cm. long, its scales
both broad and narrow, becoming paler brown upward. Blade
ca. 38 to 75 cm. long and 15 to 30 broad just above base,
tapering uniformly upward to an acuminate tip. Pinnae
elongate-lanceolate, deeply lobed, the lower 1 or 2 pairs
often narrowed at base and undulate outward. Sori borne
from tip nearly to blade-base, the fertile pinnae uniform
with the sterile; position close to midvein or occasionally
approaching medial. Sterile fronds difficult to distinguish
from those of the other moist-soil Wood Ferns.

RANGE: Incompletely known, this taxon being often confused
with others. Reported in the Dismal Swamp area of Camden
Co., N.C., from farther south in this state, and S.C. [Scat-
tered in the s. uplands, Ga. to N.C. Recently found also up
to N.J. and N.Y.]

HABITAT: Shallowly rooted in moist humus, old stumps and
logs, in swamps. Soil moderately to strongly acid.

CULTURE: Has proved easy to grow in a damp, shady, humus-
rich garden, spreading by spores. Seemingly more tolerant
of winter cold than summer heat.

NOMENCLATURE:

Dryopteris celsa Small, 1938. (S)
(*D. goldiana* ssp. *celsa* W. Palmer, 1899, basionym.)

This taxon has been much misunderstood. It was long interpreted as a hybrid between two northern members of the genus,
D. clintoniana and *D. goldiana,* neither of which grows to any
extent near it. When its spores were studied, however, they
proved, though variable, to represent not a hybrid but a species.
This was confirmed by cytologic study, it being a tetraploid,
originating as a cross between two diploids, with later chromosome-doubling.

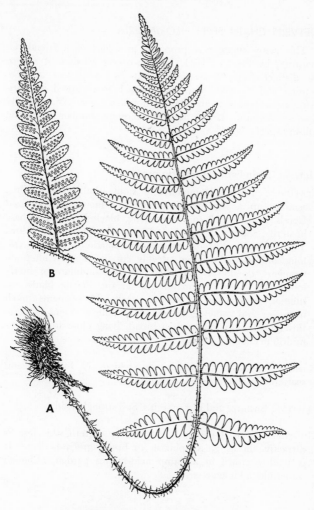

LOG FERN : *Dryopteris celsa*
A. Plant, reduced.   B. Fertile pinna.

NETVEIN CHAIN FERN : *LORINSÈRIA*

This genus name was proposed in honor of a friend, G. Lorinser, by Presl in 1851. Some workers consider it not to be distinct from *Woodwardia,* but its completely areolate veining and marked dimorphism are here regarded as justifying its segregation; an alleged intermediate in Asia actually does not resemble it. The basal chromosome number is 35. The solitary species is:

Netvein Chain Fern : *Lorinsèria areolàta*

FEATURES: Rootstock moderately stout, shallowly creeping, sending up a row of dimorphic deciduous medium-sized fronds. Stipe *ca.* 18 to 35 cm. long, blackish brown at base in sterile, and throughout in fertile fronds, sparse scaly below. Tissue glossy and bronzy green. Sterile blade *ca.* 18 to 35 cm. long and 10 to 20 broad, deeply cut into spaced alternate segments, the lower pinna-like; margins undulate or rarely lobed and finely but manifestly serrate. Fertile blade autumnal, tending to exceed the sterile, its segments much narrower and some often set off as pinnae. Veins areolate throughout. Sori longer than broad, lying close to segment-midrib in chain-like rows.

RANGE: Practically throughout our region. [N. lowlands, and scattered in both s. and n. uplands.]

HABITAT: Swamps and bog margins. Soil strongly acid.

CULTURE: Even though not cut in lacy pattern, this fern is attractive in its glossy pinkish to bronzy-green herbage. It is readily grown in a damp acid-humus garden, although sometimes a bit aggressive.

NOMENCLATURE:

Lorinseria areolata Presl, 1851. (S)
(*Acrostichum areolatum* L., 1753, basionym.)
Woodwardia angustifolia J. E. Smith, 1793, not valid.
Woodwardia areolata Moore, 1857.

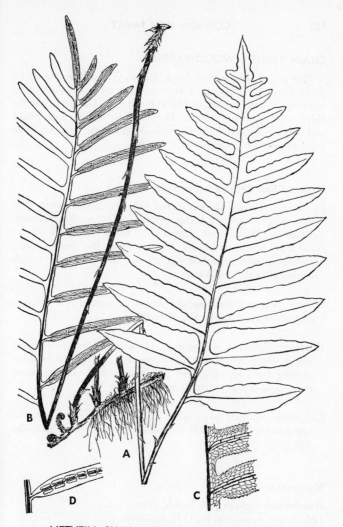

NETVEIN CHAIN FERN : *Lorinseria areolata*

A. Plant with sterile frond, reduced.
B. Fertile frond, reduced. Base of: C. Sterile and
D. Fertile segments.

CHAIN FERNS : WOODWÁRDIA

This genus was named for a friend, T. J. Woodward, by J. E. Smith in 1793. It is characterized by a stout creeping rootstock, coarse brown or blackish stipe, and large blade divided into alternate pinnae. The sori are longer than broad and form rows on chain-like vein-areoles along midribs. The basal chromosome number is 34 to 36.

Eastern Chain Fern : *Woodwárdia virgínica*

FEATURES: Fronds thick-textured but deciduous, borne in a row. Stipe shining blackish brown, *ca.* 30 to 60 cm. long. Blade *ca.* 35 to 70 cm. long and 15 to 30 broad, the pinnae cut into acutish segments. Veins beyond the areoles along midrib in part branched but all free at tip. Fertile fronds arising after the sterile ones.

RANGE: Nearly throughout our region. [Scattered in s. uplands and widespread northward; Bermuda.]

HABITAT: Various wet situations, often rooted in water-logged soil in which few if any other ferns can thrive. Soil reaction varying from strongly acid to circumneutral. Unlike many ferns, does best in sunny places.

CULTURE: Spreads too rapidly for ordinary garden use, but ornamental and desirable for muddy barrens where little else will grow.

NOMENCLATURE:

Woodwardia virginica J. E. Smith, 1793.
(*Blechnum virginicum* L., 1771, basionym.)
Anchistea virginica Presl, 1851. (S)

The basal chromosome number of this taxon has been reported as either 35 or 36, that of typical *Woodwardia* as 34. This suggests that its segregation as the "genus" *Anchistea* may be justified, but further study is needed.

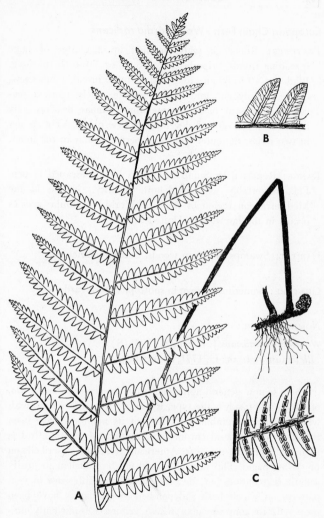

EASTERN CHAIN FERN : *Woodwardia virginica*
A. Plant, reduced. B. Sterile and C. Fertile segments.

European Chain Fern : *Woodwárdia rádicans*

FEATURES: Rootstock scaly, sending up a cluster of huge spreading fronds. Stipe lustrous brown, *ca.* 30 to 60 cm. long. Blade *ca.* 40 to 80 cm. long and 25 to 50 broad. Pinnae few, coarse, deeply cut into long-acuminate finely toothed segments. Rachis at base of some upper pinnae bearing scaly buds which fall off and develop into new plants. Vein areoles in two series, the outer elongated perpendicular to the inner.

RANGE: Reported by Small (1938) as having escaped in pen. Fla., regrettably without definite locality. [Native in the Mediterranean region of the Old World.] A similar species occurs in the far western United States.

HABITAT: Swamps or damp woods. Soil circumneutral.

CULTURE: Sometimes grown in subtropical fern gardens.

NOMENCLATURE:

Woodwardia radicans J. E. Smith, 1793. (S)
(*Blechnum radicans* L., 1771, basionym.)

There is now general agreement that the genus *Woodwardia,* of which this taxon is the type, is distinct from *Blechnum,* with which Linnaeus combined it. Two of its members have been found to have a basal chromosome number of 34, slightly less than that of the two east-American relatives, described on preceding pages. This in itself would not be sufficient to justify generic segregation, but there is a correlated difference in vein pattern, on which basis independent genus names have been proposed. In contrast, taxa whose veining is sufficiently uniform to be retained within the genus *Blechnum,* have been found to vary in chromosome number from 34 down to 28. The taxonomy of the *Blechnum* group of ferns thus manifestly needs further consideration.

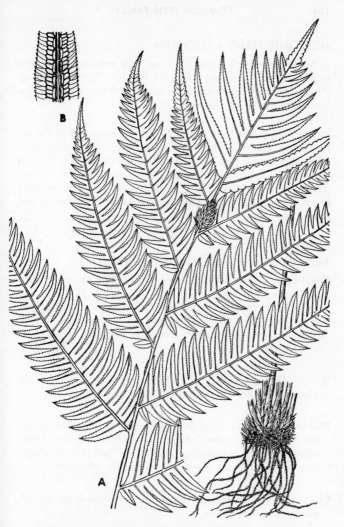

EUROPEAN CHAIN FERN : *Woodwardia radicans*

A. Plant, reduced.   B. Portion of fertile segment.

MID-SORUS FERNS : *BLÉCHNUM*

An ancient Greek name for some now unknown plant was applied to this genus by Linnaeus in 1753. There are about 20 species in the Southern Hemisphere and the world tropics, 2 of them extending into southeastern U.S.

The rootstock is long and branched, creeping and at the tip ascending. The tissue is firm with marginal thickening, often shiny and bronzy green in hue. Adjoining the midrib lie long strips of massed sporangia, with a heavy vein at outer margin. These are early covered by a red indusium, which at maturity becomes obscured. The outer veins are simple or forked and free at tip.

Toothed Mid-sorus Fern : *Bléchnum serrulàtum*

FEATURES: Rootstock stout, fine-scaly, sending up sparse tufts of fronds. Stipe dull green, scaly below, *ca.* 25 to 50 cm. long. Blade pinnate throughout, tipped by a pinna-like segment, *ca.* 30 to 60 cm. long and 13 to 25 broad. Pinnae alternate, serrate-margined, jointed at base and breaking off at maturity.

RANGE: Fla. up to St. Johns and Hernando cos.; found here in 1789. [Widespread in world tropics.]

HABITAT: Meadows, swamps, and fresh-water marshes, in the latter tending to ascend humus hummocks and tree bases; often becoming conspicuous after fires. Though increasingly rare northward, can manifestly withstand light frost.

CULTURE: Too coarse and spreading too pervasively for admission to a fern garden.

NOMENCLATURE:

Blechnum serrulatum Richard, 1792. (S)
B. indicum of some workers, not Burman, 1768.

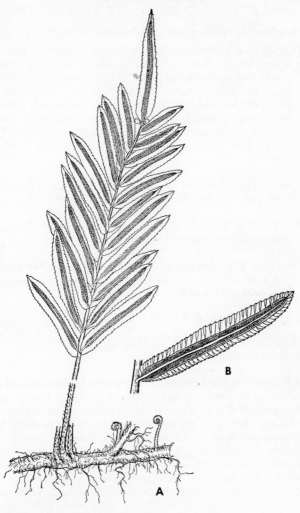

TOOTHED MID-SORUS FERN : *Blechnum serrulatum*

A. Plant, reduced.   B. Fertile pinna.

New World Mid-sorus Fern : *Bléchnum occidentàlè*

FEATURES: Rootstock slender, sending up at intervals tufts of
a few fronds. Tissue pink when young, becoming bronzy
green, and then reddish in age. Stipe bronzy, coarse scaly
below and hairy upward, *ca.* 13 to 25 cm. long. Blade oblong-
triangular, *ca.* 15 to 30 cm. long and 6 to 12 broad, pinnate
below and ending upward in a long-tapering, deeply lobed
tip. Pinnae subopposite, sessile, broad-based, subfalcate, the
fertile ones long-acuminate, entire or obscurely toothed
upward.

RANGE: Fla., Hernando Co. to Alachua Co., where found in
1916, and Iberville Par., La., in 1942. [Trop. Amer.]

HABITAT: Open woods, often in loamy soil over limestone, or
in damp depressions; soil circumneutral.

CULTURE: The attractive habit and coloring of this fern render
it a most desirable garden subject. Its range indicates that
it can withstand mild frost.

NOMENCLATURE:

Blechnum "orientale" L., 1753, a slip, corrected to:
Blechnum occidentale L., 1763. (S)

The restricted distribution of this fern is here interpreted as
indicating that it is a relatively recent arrival in Florida and
Louisiana. Had it been in our region for the many millions of
years since Oligocene geologic time, as has been postulated for
various rare taxa which occur in northwestern peninsular
Florida, it would surely have had time to become more widespread. In contrast, the preceding taxon, judging from its much
wider range, may well have started from spores brought in
by a hurricane soon after the peninsula emerged from the sea
at the close of the last interglacial stage some 75,000 years
ago; while the present one could have spread over its two tiny
areas in far less time. Whether the disjunct occurrences in
Fla. and La. represent independent introductions from the
tropics, or transportation of spores 500 miles from one to the
other, is indeterminate.

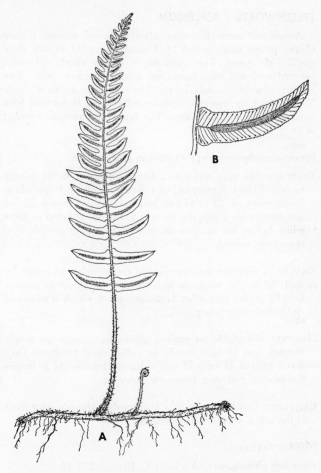

NEW WORLD MID-SORUS FERN : *Blechnum occidentale*

A. Plant, reduced.   B. Fertile pinna.

SPLEENWORTS : *ASPLÈNIUM*

An ancient name for some plant supposed to cure disease of the spleen was applied by Linnaeus in 1753 to this large world-wide genus. The rootstock is mostly short and erect, covered with old stipe-bases, and bearing narrow scales. Two elliptic vascular strands in the lower stipe unite to a single X-shaped group upward. Vein-branches bear linear sori with a narrow glabrous indusium. The basal chromosome number is 36.

Brown-stem Spleenwort : *Asplènium platyneùron*

FEATURES (of TYPE VARIETY): Short stipe and rachis shining brown. Blades dimorphic, the sterile small and spreading; fertile erect, *ca.* 23 to 45 cm. long and 2.5 to 5 broad. Pinnae alternate, with a superior auricle, gradually reduced to mere wings below, the margins finely serrate and tip acutish. Sori numerous, medial.

RANGE: A common fern practically throughout our region [as well as in the southern uplands and northeastern states]. Locally grades into other varieties, one of which is discussed on the following text-page.

HABITAT: Adaptable to various situations, though seemingly thriving best in open woods, in well-drained locations. Does about as well in subacid soil of humus hummocks as in circumneutral soil over limestone outcrops.

CULTURE: Can be grown in a fern garden, though short-lived if the soil is very rich in nutrients.

NOMENCLATURE:

Asplenium platyneuron Oakes *ex* D. C. Eaton, 1878. (S)
(*Acrostichum platyneuros* L., 1753; *platyneuron,* 1763, basionym.)
Asplenium ebeneum Aiton, 1789, later epithet.

This fern is remarkable in extending from the southern tip of Florida to western Maine without essential change in aspect, except for becoming smaller northward.

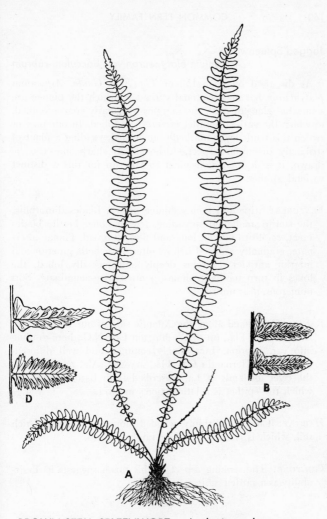

BROWN-STEM SPLEENWORT : *Asplenium platyneuron*

A. Plant, reduced.   Pinnae of: B. Type variety.
C. Incised variety.   D. Frilled form.

Jagged Spleenwort :
Asplènium platyneùron var. bácculum-rùbrum

As discussed on page 158 of *The Fern Guide*, *Asplenium platyneuron* has an occasional variant in which the pinnae are somewhat elongate with the margins irregularly coarse-toothed, to which the varietal epithet *incisum* is applied. In our present region this tendency is markedly intensified, yielding a plant of strikingly dissimilar aspect. Although no sharp line can be drawn, it is deemed convenient to take up for this a distinct varietal epithet.

FEATURES: Stipe and rachis shining brown. Blades dimorphic, the sterile small and spreading, few or none. Fertile blades erect, *ca.* 40 to 60 cm. long and 6 to 12 broad. Pinnae alternate, gradually reduced below, often with both superior and inferior auricles. Margins deeply and jaggedly lobed, the lobes in turn toothed; pinna-tip often long-acuminate. Sori numerous, near midrib.

RANGE: Occasional along the Atlantic side of our region, from Brevard Co., Fla., up to Washington Co., N.C., here grading into var. *incisum*. Increasingly common and well differentiated from Hernando Co., Fla., across s. Ala. and Miss. to the river lowlands of La. Described from Baton Rouge (of which the epithet is a latinization) in 1871.

HABITAT: Chiefly on thinly wooded slopes over mineral-rich soil, which is circumneutral or rarely subacid.

CULTURE: The striking aspect of this taxon suggests its desirability as a garden subject.

NOMENCLATURE:

Asplenium platyneuron var. *bacculum-rubrum* Fernald, 1936.
(*A. ebeneum* var. *bacculum-rubrum* Featherman, 1871, basionym.)
A. platyneuron var. *euroaustrinum* Fernald, 1934.

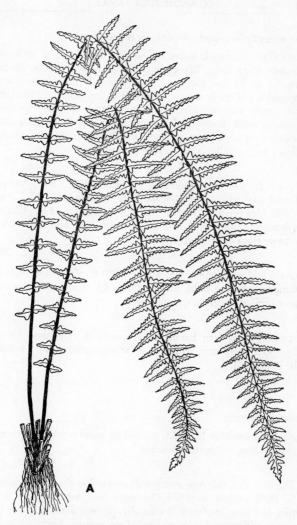

JAGGED SPLEENWORT : *A. platyneuron v. bacculum-rubrum*

A. Plant, reduced.

One-sorus Spleenwort : *Asplènium monánthes*

FEATURES: Rootstock fine-scaly, sending up a tuft of uniform fronds. Stipe short, like rachis blackish brown, bristly. Blade *ca.* 13 to 25 cm. long and 1 to 2 broad. Pinnae close-set, opposite, obliquely oblong, attached at lower corner, toothed on upper margin. Main vein lying toward lower pinna-margin, with few-forked fine veins arising from it. Sorus solitary on each pinna, beyond middle of main vein, sometimes with smaller companions farther out.

RANGE: In the low mountains of Oconee Co., S.C., where found in 1946, and adjacent Transylvania Co., N.C., in 1952. Also reported from a sink in Alachua Co., Fla. [World subtropics and tropical uplands; extending into sw. U.S., remote from our region.]

HABITAT: Mossy granite ledges at *ca.* 800 ft. alt., where winter temperatures are mild, and lowland sink walls, cool in summer. Soil subacid to circumneutral.

CULTURE: This fern having no ornamental value and being here extremely rare, its removal for attempted culture would be ill-advised.

NOMENCLATURE:

Asplenium monanthes L., 1753; altered by some workers, without justification, to *"monanthemum."*

The fact that this fern was not discovered in the southeastern U.S. until as late as 1946 illustrates how incompletely this region has been explored botanically. It may indeed prove to be more widespread than at present recognized, being difficult to tell at a distance from the ubiquitous Brownstem Spleenwort. Over its range the One-sorus Spleenwort is markedly variable; the spores which started our colonies were presumably brought in by a hurricane from Mexico, where similar forms occur.

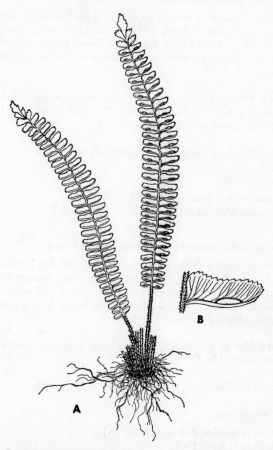

ONE-SORUS SPLEENWORT : *Asplenium monanthes*

A. Plant, reduced. B. Pinna.

Black-stem Spleenwort : *Asplènium resíliens*

FEATURES: Rootstock bearing copious long blackish scales. Stipe short, black. Rachis black with narrow green wings toward tip. Blade *ca.* 13 to 25 cm. long and 2 broad. Pinnae opposite, with low superior auricle and undulate upper margin. Sori medial.

RANGE: Poorly known, many reports representing hybrids; disjunct in Berkeley Co., S.C., nw. Fla., and Winn Par., La. [Upland valleys, se. U.S.; trop. Amer.]

HABITAT: On limestone; soil circumneutral. Not cult'd.

NOMENCLATURE:

Asplenium resiliens Kunze, 1844. (S)
A. parvulum Martens & Galeotti, 1840, preoccupied.

Varicolored Spleenwort : *Asplènium heterochròum*

FEATURES: Similar to the above species, but differing in: Rootstock-scales few, short, brown. Rachis grading upward from black to brown with conspicuous green stripes and wings, to which the epithet refers. Blade to 3 cm. broad. Upper pinnamargin serrate. Sori toward midrib.

RANGE: Not as yet known, but probably scattered over Fla. [Bermuda and W.I.]

HABITAT: On limestone; soil circumneutral. Not cult'd.

NOMENCLATURE:

Asplenium heterochroum Kunze, 1834. (S)
A. muticum Gilbert, 1903.

Both the above taxa are variable cytologically—from diploid to octoploid—and hybridize with one another. A hybrid which is pentaploid, and seemingly reproduces only vegetatively, ranges widely over Fla. and up to Jones Co., N.C., growing mostly on soft limestones. This has been named *Asplènium heteroresíliens* Wagner, 1963.

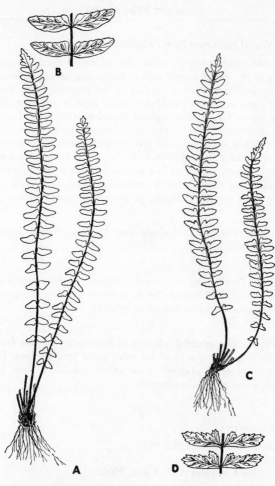

BLACK-STEM SPLEENWORT : *Asplenium resiliens*
A. Plant, reduced. B. Pinnae.

VARICOLORED SPLEENWORT : *Asplenium heterochroum*
C. Plant, reduced. D. Pinnae.

New World Birds-nest Fern : *Asplènium serràtum*

FEATURES: Aspect wholly unlike that of any of the other members of the genus in our region, suggesting, as the colloquial name indicates, a small edition of the tropical Asian Birdsnest Fern, as well as the Harts-tongue Fern, a northern taxon ranging as far south as upland limestone valleys of Tennessee. Rootstock stout, scaly, as is also the very short stipe. Fronds few, in a vase-like group. Blade undivided, tapering about equally toward both ends, *ca.* 40 to 80 cm. long and 6 to 12 broad, serrate or in a rare variant cut-toothed upward, smooth and shining. Veins numerous, close-set, forked near base. Sori medial, elongate, in ascending parallel rows.

RANGE: S. Fla. up to Volusia and Lee cos.; found here in 1877. [Trop. Amer.]

HABITAT: Perched on tree trunks, stumps, humus hummocks, and sometimes limestone ledges in dense woods and swamps; soil circumneutral or less often subacid.

CULTURE: The graceful clusters of strikingly lustrous fronds make this a good subject for subtropical fern gardens. It is easy to grow if planted in an ample container, kept well shaded and in a moist atmosphere.

NOMENCLATURE:

Asplenium serratum L., 1753. (S)

TOOTHED VARIANT:

A. serratum f. *incisum* A. A. Eaton, 1906.

Were only the species of our region to be considered, the present one with its undivided blade and close-set parallel veins might be deemed worthy of treatment as an independent genus. When, however, the 600 or more occurring over the world are taken into account, there prove to be so many intermediate states of such characters that it is manifestly unrealistic to base taxonomic segregates upon them.

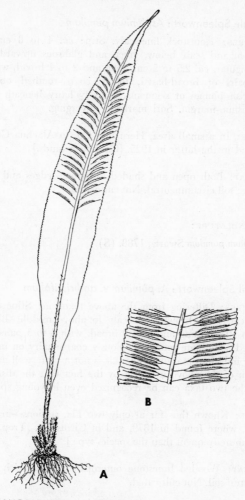

NEW-WORLD BIRDS-NEST FERN : *Asplenium serratum*

A. Plant, reduced.   B. Section of fertile blade.

Triangle Spleenwort : *Asplènium pùmilum*

FEATURES: Rootstock fine-scaly. Stipe *ca.* 4 to 8 cm. long, brown and scaly below, green and glabrous upward. Blade triangular, *ca.* 2.5 to 5 cm. long and 2 to 4 broad, with 1 or 2 pairs of broad-based, lobed, coarse-toothed obtuse to acutish pinnae or segments, sparsely hairy beneath and on indusium-margin. Sori markedly diverging.

RANGE: In a small area, Hernando Co. to Alachua Co., Fla.; found in the latter in 1925. [Caribbean lands.]

HABITAT: Both open and shaded limestone ledges and rims of sinks; soil circumneutral. Not cultivated.

NOMENCLATURE:

Asplenium pumilum Swartz, 1788. (S)

Chervil Spleenwort : *A. pùmilum* v. *anthriscifòlium*

FEATURES: Differing from the above taxon in: Stipe *ca.* 8 to 15 cm. long, brown and scaly to above middle. Blade *ca.* 5 to 10 cm. long and 4 to 8 broad, with 3 to 5 pairs of cut-lobed acuminate pinnae, copiously coarse-hairy on underside and indusium-margin. That this is not a mere well-nourished form of the above is shown by the fact that the distinctness of the two taxa can be recognized even in young sporelings.

RANGE: Known thus far at only two Fla. stations—in Marion Co., where found in 1879, and in Citrus Co. [Trop. Amer., far more frequent than the species type.]

HABITAT: Wooded limestone outcrops, in humus-rich circumneutral soil. Not cultivated.

NOMENCLATURE:

Asplenium pumilum var. *anthriscifolium* Wherry, p. 346.
(*A. anthriscifolium* Jacquin, 1788, basionym.)
A. adiantum-nigrum on Fla. labels, not L., 1753.

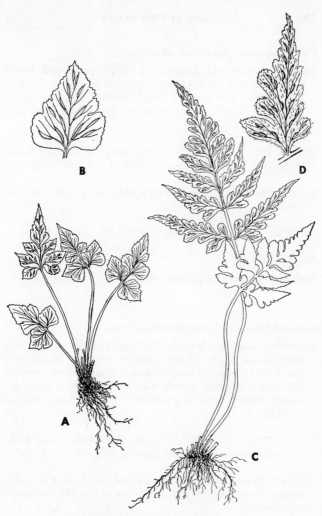

TRIANGLE SPLEENWORT : *Asplenium pumilum*

A. Plant. B. Pinna, enlarged.

CHERVIL SPLEENWORT : *A. pumilum* v. *anthriscifolium*

C. Plant. D. Pinna, enlarged.

Cut Spleenwort : *Asplènium abscíssum*

FEATURES: Rootstock brown-scaly. Stipe green and brown striped, *ca.* 8 to 15 cm. long. Blade subtriangular, *ca.* 8 to 15 cm. long and 6 to 12 broad, divided into few spaced fine-serrate pinnae with obscure superior auricle. Sori near midrib.

RANGE: Fla., in two disjunct areas, Dade Co., and Hernando to Alachua cos.; found here in 1878. [Caribbean lands.]

HABITAT: Wooded limestone ledges and walls of sinks; soil circumneutral.

CULTURE: Has proved difficult to establish in rock gardens.

NOMENCLATURE:

Asplenium abscissum Willdenow, 1810. (S)

Auricled Spleenwort : *Asplènium aurìtum*

FEATURES: Rootstock brown-scaly. Stipe *ca.* 8 to 15 cm. long, brown below. Blade oblong-triangular, *ca.* 15 to 30 cm. long and 5 to 10 broad. Pinnae close-set, short-stalked, jaggedly cut, with a superior auricle which in the larger more dissected southern forms is set off as a pinnule. Sorus position variable.

RANGE: Fla., in two disjunct areas, Dade–Collier and Hillsborough–Sumter cos.; found here in 1895. [Trop. Amer.]

HABITAT: Perched on remotely isolated dead trees in damp woods; soil subacid. Fronds shriveling in drought, but reviving after rain.

CULTURE: Readily grown on humus hummocks, though seemingly requiring more moisture than in its native haunts.

NOMENCLATURE:

Asplenium auritum Swartz, 1801.

CUT SPLEENWORT : *Asplenium abscissum*
A. Plant, reduced.   B. Pinna.

AURICLED SPLEENWORT : *Asplenium auritum*
C. Plant, reduced.   D. Pinna.

171

Hemlock Spleenwort : *Asplènium cristàtum*

FEATURES: Rootstock fibrous-scaly. Stipe *ca.* 8 to 15 cm. long, brown and green striped. Blade shining bright green, *ca.* 10 to 20 cm. long and 6 to 12 broad, lacy-cut. Sori medial.

RANGE: Sumter Co. to Citrus Co., Fla.; found here in 1878. [Trop. Amer.]

HABITAT: Wooded limestone ledges, not far from standing water; soil circumneutral.

CULTURE: The lacy bright-green fronds would be attractive in a rock garden, but it is difficult to establish.

NOMENCLATURE:

Asplenium cristatum Lamarck, 1786. (S)

Ruffled Spleenwort : *Asplènium* ✕ *plènum*

FEATURES: Rootstock fine-scaly, sending up a tuft of arching fronds. Stipe brown-striped, *ca.* 5 to 10 cm. long. Blade *ca.* 8 to 15 cm. long and 3.5 to 7 broad, bipinnate with close-set divisions. Sori few, long, medial.

RANGE: Seemingly rare, and thus far known only at one station each in Citrus, Sumter, and Alachua cos., Fla. Discovered in the first in 1936.

HABITAT: Walls of sinks and wooded limestone ledges; soil circumneutral. Not cultivated.

NOMENCLATURE:

Asplenium [✕] *plenum* E. P. St. John, 1938. (S)
A. abscissum ✕ *cristatum* Wagner, 1963.
    SHADE-FORM:
A. "subtile" E. P. St. John, 1938. (S)
    This is deemed not to merit any nomenclatorial recognition, as a visit to the type locality, a deep well-like sink near Lecanto, Citrus Co., Fla., showed it to intergrade with better lighted *A.* ✕ *plenum*.

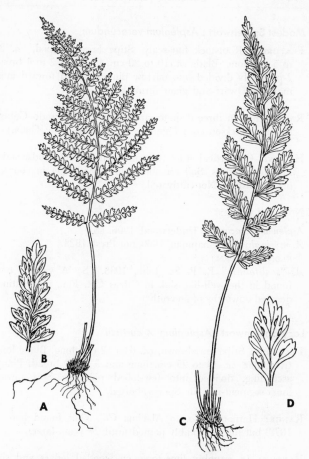

HEMLOCK SPLEENWORT : *Asplenium cristatum*

A. Plant.   B. Pinna, enlarged.

RUFFLED SPLEENWORT : *Asplenium × plenum*

C. Plant.   D. Pinna, enlarged.

Modest Spleenwort : *Asplènium verecúndum*

FEATURES: Rootstock fine-scaly. Stipe brown-striped, *ca.* 2.5 to 5 cm. long. Blade *ca.* 10 to 20 cm. long and 2 to 4 broad, 2-pinnately divided into narrow pinnules. Sori toward inner margins. Dwarf and giant forms known.

RANGE: Fla. in three disjunct areas: Dade, Hernando–Columbia, and Jackson cos.; found in the last in 1840. [Cuba.]

HABITAT: On vertical or overhanging walls of sinks, and wooded limestone ledges. Soil circumneutral, dryish, yet in continuously moist air. Not cultivated.

NOMENCLATURE:

Asplenium verecundum Underwood, 1906. (S)
A. myriophyllum Chapman, 1860, not Presl, 1823.
   ELONGATE FORM:
A. "scalifolium" E. P. St. John, 1938. (S) A variant once found in the well-like sink in Citrus Co., Fla., now extinct, deemed unworthy of an epithet.

Lacy Spleenwort : *Asplènium* × *curtissii*

FEATURES: Stipe gray-brown, *ca.* 6 to 12 cm. long. Blade long-triangular, *ca.* 13 to 25 cm. long and 5 to 10 broad. Pinnae ascending, divided into few-lobed pinnules. Sori toward inner segment-margin. Spores aborted.

RANGE: Hernando Co. to Alachua Co., Fla.; found here in 1879, but not acceptably named until 27 years later.

HABITAT: In crumbly limestone, on wooded ledges and sink walls, often becoming abundant for a time, and then dwindling or vanishing. Not cultivated.

NOMENCLATURE:

Asplenium [×] **curtissii** Underwood, 1906. (S)
A. abscissum × **verecundum** Wagner, 1962.
(Chromosome nos. of these resp. 36 and 72, of the hybrid 108.)
A. myriophyllum on Curtiss labels, not Presl, 1825.

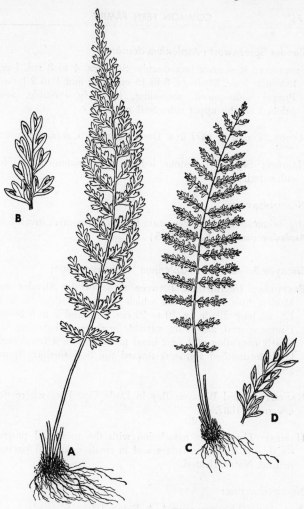

LACY SPLEENWORT : *Asplenium* × *curtissii*
A. Plant.   B. Pinna, enlarged.

MODEST SPLEENWORT : *Asplenium verecundum*
C. Plant.   D. Pinna, enlarged.

175

Slender Spleenwort : *Asplènium dentàtum*

FEATURES: Rootstock brown-scaly. Stipe *ca.* 4 to 8 cm. long, brown at base. Blade *ca.* 8 to 15 cm. long and 1 to 2 broad. Pinnae wide-spaced, ascending, obliquely rhombic, few-toothed on the upper side. Sori medial.

RANGE: Found in 1877 in s. Dade Co., Fla. [Caribbean lands.]

HABITAT: Shaded limestone ledges; soil circumneutral. Not cultivated.

NOMENCLATURE:

Asplenium trichomanes dentatum L., 1753, trinomial, invalid.
Asplenium dentatum L., 1759. (S)

Biscayne Spleenwort : *Asplènium* × *biscayneànum*

FEATURES: Intermediate between those of the Slender and Modest Spleenworts, with which it grows. Stipe *ca.* 6 to 12 cm. long. Blade *ca.* 10 to 20 cm. long and 2 to 4 broad. Pinnae spaced, ascending, variable in shape and cutting, but mostly consisting of 1 or 2 basal pinnules with a few irregular blunt-toothed segments toward tip. Sori medial. Spores aborted.

RANGE: Around Biscayne Bay in Dade Co., Fla., where discovered in 1887.

HABITAT: Growing in association with the presumed parents on shaded limestone ledges and in small sinks; soil circumneutral. Not cultivated.

NOMENCLATURE:

Asplenium [×] *biscayneanum* A. A. Eaton, 1904. (S)
(*A. rhizophyllum* var. *biscayneanum* D. C. Eaton, 1887, basionym; in this connection it should be noted that the species here listed was not the northern one which Linnaeus first so-named, now known as *Camptosorus*, but a tropical one which he confusedly named later.)
A. dentatum × "*myriophyllum*" -*verecundum*, Holden, 1887.

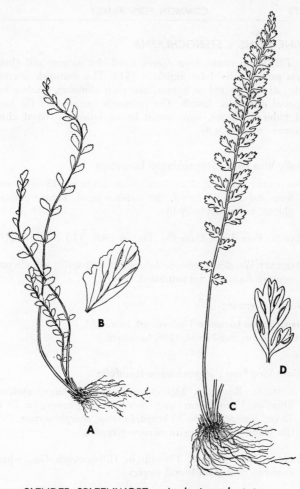

SLENDER SPLEENWORT : *Asplenium dentatum*

A. Plant. B. Pinna, enlarged.

BISCAYNE SPLEENWORT : *Asplenium* × *biscayneanum*

C. Plant. D. Pinna, enlarged.

177

VINE FERNS : *STENOCHLAÈNA*

This genus name, from Greek words for narrow and cloak, was proposed by John Smith in 1842. The rootstock is cord-like, at first rooted in humus, and then climbing, sending out spaced dimorphic fronds. The sporangia spread over the back of reduced pinnae, unprotected by an indusium. Basal chromosome number is 37.

Holly Vine Fern : *Stenochlaèna kunzeàna*

FEATURES: Stipe *ca.* 4 to 8 cm. long. Blade *ca.* 15 to 30 cm. long and 5 to 10 broad, the rachis winged. Pinnae elliptic-oblong, somewhat holly-like.

RANGE: Found in s. Dade Co., Fla., in 1903. [W.I.]

HABITAT: Wooded limestone ledges and sink walls; soil circum-neutral. Rare and not cultivated.

NOMENCLATURE:

Stenochlaena kunzeana Underwood, 1906. (S)
(*Olfersia kunzeana* Presl, 1836, basionym.)

Giant Vine Fern : *Stenochlaèna tenuifòlia*

FEATURES: Rootstock high-climbing; fronds large, arching. Stipe *ca.* 13 to 25 cm. long. Sterile blade pinnate, *ca.* 38 to 75 cm. long and 25 to 50 broad, lustrous, sharply serrate. Fertile blade 2-pinnate with narrow pinnules.

RANGE: Escaped in s. Fla. up to Hillsborough Co., where found in 1932. [Old World tropics.]

HABITAT: Woodland humus and tree trunks. Soil subacid.

CULTURE: Spreads widely in mild-climate woods gardens.

NOMENCLATURE:

Stenochlaena tenuifolia Moore, 1856. (S)
(*Lomaria tenuifolia* Desvaux, 1811, basionym.)

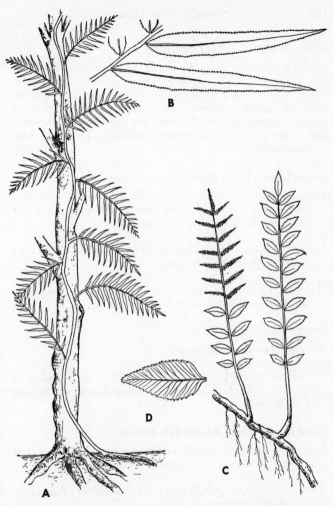

GIANT VINE FERN : *Stenochlaena tenuifolia*

A. Plant climbing tree, reduced.   B. Sterile pinnae.

HOLLY VINE FERN : *Stenochlaena kunzeana*

C. Plant, reduced.   D. Sterile pinna.

LEATHER FERNS : *ACRÓSTICHUM*

This genus name, from the Greek for terminal rows (of fertile structures) was proposed by Linnaeus in 1753. It is now restricted to a small group of tall ferns. These have a stout rootstock which sends up close-set, short-stiped, pinnate, leathery-textured fronds. The veins are areolate and the sporangia form a felt-like coating beneath pinnae. The basal chromosome number is 30.

Inland Leather Fern : *Acróstichum excélsum*

FEATURES: Height to *ca.* 500 cm. Pinnae close-set, hairy beneath, many fertile. Areoles narrow, diverging from the midrib not far from perpendicular.

RANGE: Fla., somewhat inland, up to St. Johns and Citrus cos.; found here in 1843. [Trop. Amer.]

HABITAT: Fresh-water marshes and swamps; soil circumneutral. Too massive for much horticultural use.

NOMENCLATURE:

Acrostichum excelsum Maxon, 1905.
A. lomarioides Jenman, 1898, preoccupied.
(*A. danaeaefolium* Langsdorf & Fischer, 1810, often applied to this taxon (S), but clearly described as having the veining of the following one.)

Coast Leather Fern : *Acróstichum aùreum*

FEATURES: Height to *ca.* 300 cm. Pinnae spaced, glabrous, few terminal fertile. Areoles broad, sloping up at 45°.

RANGE: Fla. coasts, up to Volusia and Pinellas cos.; found here in 1789. [World tropics.]

HABITAT: Salt marshes, mangrove swamps, and wet sinks; soil circumneutral, brackish. Not cultivated.

NOMENCLATURE:

Acrostichum aureum L., 1753. (S)

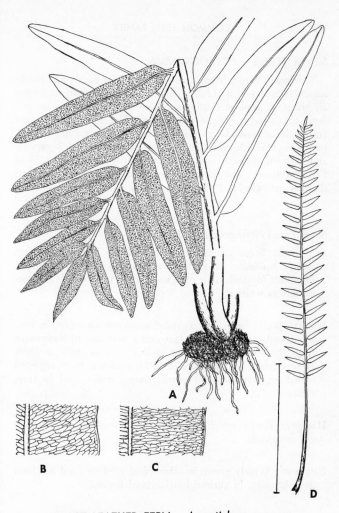

COAST LEATHER FERN : *Acrostichum aureum*

A. Parts of plant, reduced.   B. Section of pinna.

INLAND LEATHER FERN : *A. excelsum*

C. Section of pinna.   D. Frond with human-height rule.

SILVER FERNS : *PITYROGRÁMMA*

This genus name, from the Greek words for mealy and markings, was proposed by Link in 1833; the same author, forgetting all about it, applied *Ceropteris,* from the Greek for wax and fern, to the genus eight years later. The rootstock is erect and scaly, and sends up close-set fronds. Their stipe is dark brown to blackish and shining. The blade is 1- to 3-pinnate, and covered beneath with powdery wax (white, or in "Gold Ferns" yellow). The sporangia are borne in strips along veins; there is no indusium. The basal chromosome number is 30.

Silver Fern : *Pityrográmma calomelànos*

FEATURES: Stipe *ca.* 20 to 40 cm. long. Blade triangular, mostly 2-pinnate, *ca.* 25 to 50 cm. long and 13 to 25 broad. Pinnulets toothed, their margins tending to reflex. Wax coating silvery white.

RANGE: While sometimes regarded as merely an escape in Fla., this is contradicted by the fact that it was sent to Rafinesque from some unrecorded point in this state as early as 1836. It was found in Polk Co. in 1931, and has been reported elsewhere, but does not persist long. [Widespread in trop. Amer.]

HABITAT: Rocky woods and invading disturbed ground. Soil circumneutral.

CULTURE: Widely grown in subtropical gardens (and northern greenhouses), in various horticultural forms.

NOMENCLATURE:

Pityrogramma calomelas Link, 1833; corrected to *calomelanos* by Domin, 1928. (S)
(*Acrostichum calomelanos* L., 1753, basionym.)
Ceropteris calomelaena Link, 1841; later name, invalid, but rather widely used by horticulturists.

SILVER FERN : *Pityrogramma calomelanos*

A. Plant, reduced.   B. Fertile pinna.

SPLIT-PINNA FERNS : *TRISMÈRIA*

This genus name, from the Greek for divided into three, was proposed by Fée in 1852. There are a few species in tropical America, one ranging into Florida. The rootstock is stout and erect, sending up clustered fronds. The lower pinnae are split part way down into 2 or 3 segments. The veins are divided into close-set branches, which end in thickish teeth. The sporangia are borne in strips along veins, and while lacking an indusium are surrounded by powdery wax.

Split-Pinna Fern : *Trismèria trifoliàta*

FEATURES: Stipe dark brown, shining, grooved, *ca.* 30 to 60 cm. long. Blade *ca.* 40 to 80 cm. long and 10 to 20 broad, the lowest pinnae forked into 3, the medial ones into 2 segments, their margins obscurely toothed. Wax bright yellow.

RANGE: In a small area in Dade Co., Fla., where found in 1953; its limited extent indicates it to be a relatively recent arrival. [Widespread in trop. Amer.]

HABITAT: Moist woods, here associated with *Blechnum serrulatum,* the two looking alike at a distance. Soil circumneutral.

CULTURE: Worthy of trial in a subtropical fern garden.

NOMENCLATURE:

Trismeria trifoliata Diels, 1899.
(*Acrostichum trifoliatum* L., 1753, basionym.)
Trismeria aurea Fée, 1852, superfluous name.

This genus is manifestly closely related to *Pityrogramma,* but the unusual plan of pinna-division is deemed sufficient justification for separating them.

SPLIT-PINNA FERN : *Trismeria trifoliata*

A. Plant, reduced.

WATER FERNS : *CERATÓPTERIS*

This unusual genus was named from the Greek for antler and fern by Brongniart in 1821. The plants are succulent floating or mud-rooting annuals. The prostrate sterile blades are areolate-veined, and produce marginal buds. The erect fertile blades are cut into narrow segments which bear rows of fragile globular sporangia.

Widespread Water Fern : *Ceratópteris pteridoìdes*

FEATURES: Stipe inflated, *ca.* 5 to 10 cm. long. Sterile blade *ca.* 8 to 15 cm. long and broad; areoles few, large. Fertile blade *ca.* 15 to 30 cm. high. Annulus cells few.

RANGE: Fla. up to Seminole and Alachua cos.; found here in 1879. [Trop. Amer.]

HABITAT: In circumneutral lakes, streams, and ditches.

CULTURE: Grown in shady mild-climate water gardens.

NOMENCLATURE:

Ceratopteris pteridoides Hieronymus, 1905. (S)
(*Parkeria pteridoides* Hooker, 1825, basionym.)

Triangle Water Fern : *Ceratópteris deltoìdea*

FEATURES: Stipe not inflated, *ca.* 10 to 20 cm. long. Sterile blade *ca.* 15 to 30 cm. long and broad, with many small vein-areoles. Fertile blade *ca.* 20 to 40 cm. high. Annulus cells numerous.

RANGE: Fla., found in Charlotte Co., 1878, and Highlands Co., 1937; La., Orleans Par., 1885. [Trop. Amer.]

HABITAT and CULTURE: As in the preceding species.

NOMENCLATURE:

Ceratopteris deltoidea Benedict, 1909. (S)

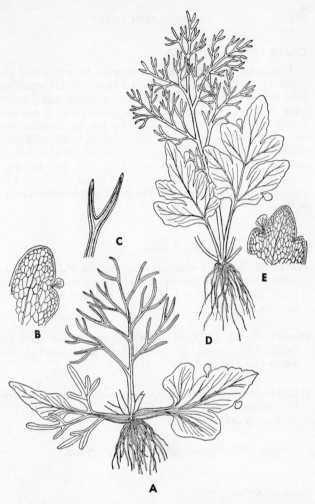

WIDESPREAD WATER FERN : *Ceratopteris pteridoides*
A. Plant, reduced. Sections of B. Sterile. C. Fertile blades.

TRIANGLE WATER FERN : *Ceratopteris deltoidea*
D. Plant, reduced. E. Section of sterile blade.

GRASS FERNS : *VITTÀRIA*

This genus name, from the Greek word for stripe, was proposed by J. E. Smith in 1793. Its members are epiphytic, with long pendent fronds lacking strengthening tissue, resembling thick grass blades. The sporangia are borne in two long narrow strips. There is no indusium, but the margins may reflex. Especially notable is the gametophyte, which unlike that of most members of the Fern Family is long and narrow, irregularly lobed, and but one cell thick. This and the other peculiarities have led some workers to assign the genus to a separate family, *Vittariaceae*. The basal chromosome number is 30.

Shoestring Fern : *Vittària lineàta*

FEATURES: Rootstock short, bearing copious iridescent scales with a long thread-like tip. Fronds clustered, barely stiped, *ca.* 30 to 60 (or rarely to 120) cm. long and 2 mm. broad, lustrous.

RANGE: Fla. up to Duval and Citrus cos.; found along the Indian River as early as 1789. Disjunct in Lincoln Co., Ga., where found in 1938. [Trop. Amer.]

HABITAT: Perched on trees, especially palmettos and oaks; in Ga., unique in growing on a south-facing sandstone cliff. Soil moderately to strongly acid.

CULTURE: Difficult to transplant and rarely grown.

NOMENCLATURE:

Vittaria lineata J. E. Smith, 1793. (S)
(*Pteris lineata* L., 1753, basionym.)

The related Broad-scale Grass Fern, **Vittària filifòlia** Fée, 1852, was found in 1960 in Collier Co., Fla. It is distinguished by only weakly iridescent scales *ca.* 3 or 4 cells broad well up toward the tip.

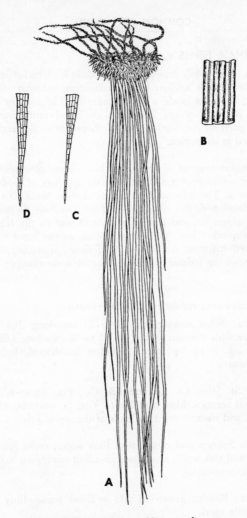

SHOESTRING FERN : *Vittaria lineata*

A. Plant, reduced.   B. Section of blade.   C. Scale, enlarged.

BROAD-SCALE S. F. : *V. filifolia*.   D. Scale, enlarged.

MAIDENHAIR FERNS : *ADIÁNTUM*

A fern which while growing in wet places kept its foliage dry was named by the ancient Greeks adiantum, meaning without moisture; this was made a genus name by Linnaeus in 1753. Around 200 species are known in the mild temperate and tropical parts of the world; four of them are native and two introduced in our region.

Our representatives of the genus have a creeping rootstock bearing slender brown scales and sending up a row of moderate-sized fronds. The stipe and rachis are shining black. No midvein is developed, the veins arising from the base of the pinnules or pinnulets, and forking repeatedly out to the free tip. Unlike any other fern, the sori are borne on the inner surface of reflexed marginal scarious flaps of tissue, imitating though not representing indusia. The basal chromosome number is 30.

Venus-hair Fern : *Adiántum capíllus-véneris*

FEATURES: Stipe arching, *ca.* 13 to 25 cm. long. Blade triangular with flexuous rachis, *ca.* 15 to 30 cm. long and 8 to 15 broad, 2- or 3-pinnate. Pinnulets fan-shaped. Indusioid flaps lunate.

RANGE: St. Johns Co. to Hernando Co., Fla., up to se. N.C. and out across s. Miss. and La. to Tex. [S. uplands, adj. ne. states, and warm-temperate lands of the world.]

HABITAT: Springs and cataracts of limy water, moist limestone cliffs, and sink walls, sometimes invading crumbling masonry. Soil circumneutral.

CULTURE: Readily grown on tufa or other porous limy rocks, but little used.

NOMENCLATURE:

Adiantum capillus-veneris L., 1753. (S)
A. c. var. *protrusum* Fernald, 1950, a variant with long rootstock-tip.

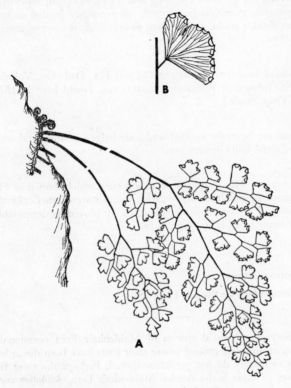

VENUS-HAIR FERN : *Adiantum capillus-veneris*

A. Plant, reduced. B. Pinnule.

Fan Maidenhair Fern : *Adiántum ténerum*

FEATURES: Stipe erect, shining, *ca.* 13 to 25 cm. long. Blade ovate, *ca.* 25 to 50 cm. long and 20 to 40 broad, repeatedly pinnate. Pinnulets fan-shaped, conspicuously jointed at base to slender stalks, and tending to break off, the upper margin lobed.

RANGE: In three disjunct areas of pen. Fla., Dade Co., Volusia–St. Johns and Hernando–Alachua cos. Found here in 1875. [Trop. Amer.]

HABITAT: Sparsely wooded limestone ledges, grottoes and walls of sinks. Soil circumneutral.

CULTURE: This beautiful plant was once widely grown in Fla. gardens, and most of its native colonies were practically destroyed by commercial collectors. It proved undependable, however, and is no longer in use.

NOMENCLATURE:

Adiantum tenerum Swartz, 1788. (S)

Several cultivated species of Maidenhair Fern occasionally turn up in waste ground where their roots have been discarded, but seemingly do not persist or spread. Perhaps the most frequent of these is the Beaded Maidenhair Fern, **Adiántum cuneàtum** Langsdorf & Fischer, 1810, from South America. This differs from the above species in being lower and thinner in texture, with smaller pinnulets not jointed to the stalk, and roundish indusioid flaps producing a beaded effect on upper margin.

One other exotic, the Rough Maidenhair Fern, has seemingly become established locally, so is described in more detail on a following text-page.

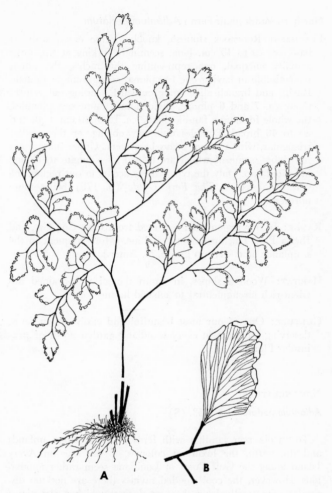

FAN MAIDENHAIR FERN : *Adiantum tenerum*

A. Plant, reduced. B. Pinnule.

Northern Maidenhair Fern : *Adiántum pedàtum*

FEATURES: Rootstock stoutish, knobby. Stipe erect, scaly at base, *ca.* 20 to 40 cm. long, seemingly forking at tip; forks actually unequal, one representing the rachis, the other, recognizable in having one less pinna, a single major branch. Rachis and branch alike curve outward, sending out respectively *ca.* 7 and 6 pinnae, divided into numerous pinnules, the whole forming a fan-like blade *ca.* 15 to 30 cm. high and 20 to 40 broad. Pinnules obliquely oblong, or the smaller triangular, with a rather heavy basal vein. Upper margin cut into lobes, some of which are tipped by a lunate to oblong indusioid flap. Only the type variety occurs in our region, the variants noted in *The Fern Guide* (p. 176) being more northern.

RANGE: In our region rare, scattered from Clay Co., Ga., and Iberia Par., La., up to the Fall Line. [More frequent in the s. uplands, and well up into n. N. Amer.]

HABITAT: Wooded slopes, in damp though well-drained nutrient-rich circumneutral to subacid humus soil.

CULTURE: One of our most beautiful and easily grown ferns, deserving inclusion in every woodland garden north of peninsular Florida.

NOMENCLATURE:

Adiantum pedatum L., 1753. (S)

To an observer familiar with ferns in the southern uplands and the north, the luxuriant colonies of this one on Avery Island along the Gulf Coast of Louisiana seem rather anomalous. However, the cool wooded ravines there are not too dissimilar climatically from those at distinctly higher elevations; and at least one other species of primarily upland and northern range—the Glade Fern, *Athyrium pycnocarpon*—also grows there, as noted on an earlier page. At the same time, the winters are mild enough to permit the survival of several subtropical ones.

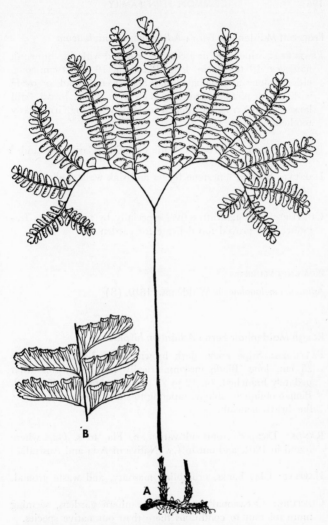

NORTHERN MAIDENHAIR FERN : *Adiantum pedatum*

A. Plant, reduced.   B. Pinnules.

Fragrant Maidenhair Fern : *Adiántum melanoleùcum*

FEATURES: Stipe erect or ascending, covered with fine brownish hairs, *ca.* 10 to 20 cm. long. Blade *ca.* 10 to 20 cm. long, either oblong and pinnate, *ca.* 1.5 to 3 cm. broad, or ovate with a few pinnate branches, then 3 to 6 cm. broad (still larger in the tropics). Pinnae obliquely oblong, irregularly toothed.

RANGE: Found in 1916 in s. Dade Co., Fla. [Caribbean lands.]

HABITAT: Shaded limestone ledges and sink walls. Soil circum-neutral.

CULTURE: Although attractive, especially by virtue of its fragrance, has proved too delicate for garden use.

NOMENCLATURE:

Adiantum melanoleucum Willdenow, 1810. (S)

Rough Maidenhair Fern : *Adiántum hispídulum*

FEATURES: Stipe erect, dark brown, bristly-hairy, *ca.* 12 to 25 cm. long. Blade unsymmetrically triangular, somewhat pedately branched, *ca.* 12 to 25 cm. long and 8 to 15 broad. Pinnae obliquely oblong, tapering to stalk, irregularly serrate, fine-bristly beneath.

RANGE: Escaped from cultivation, n. Fla. to s. Ga., where found in 1901, and out to La. [Native of Asia and Australia.]

HABITAT: Clay banks, crumbling masonry, and waste ground.

CULTURE: Occasionally grown in southern gardens, seeming more tolerant to conditions there than our native species.

NOMENCLATURE:

Adiantum hispidulum Swartz, 1801. (S)

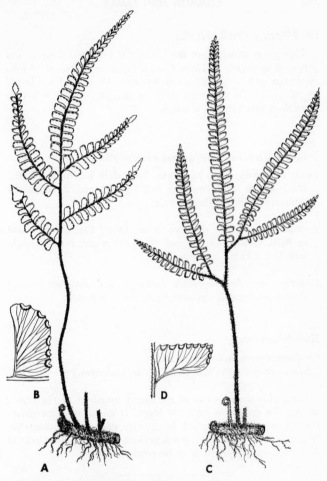

FRAGRANT MAIDENHAIR FERN : *Adiantum melanoleucum*

A. Plant, reduced.   B. Pinnule.

ROUGH MAIDENHAIR FERN : *Adiantum hispidulum*

C. Plant, reduced.   D. Pinnule.

197

LIP FERNS : *CHEILÁNTHES*

This genus name, from the Greek for marginal flowers, was proposed by Swartz in 1806. The plants are moderate-sized sub-evergreen rock ferns with 2- or 3-pinnate blade, and sori borne at enlarged vein tips near segment margins, which reflex to form short green indusioid strips.

Southern Lip Fern : *Cheilánthes microphýlla*

FEATURES: Stipe *ca.* 8 to 15 cm. long, dark brown, fine-hairy. Blade *ca.* 10 to 20 cm. long and 3 to 6 broad, 2- or basally 3-pinnate; pinnules bristly-hairy.

RANGE: Fla., in four disjunct areas: Duval Co., where found in 1878, Collier, Citrus, and Washington cos. resp. [Also in mid-Tex. and in Caribbean lands.]

HABITAT: Wooded limestone outcrops, and invading coastal shell mounds; soil circumneutral. Not cultivated.

NOMENCLATURE:

Cheilanthes microphylla Swartz, 1806. (S)
(*Adiantum microphyllum* Swartz 1788, basionym.)

Since this taxon is one of the larger members of the genus, the species epithet is certainly inapt. It had been appropriate enough when first applied by Swartz under *Adiantum;* but when transfer to another genus proved necessary, the Code of Nomenclature required it to be retained.

A closely related taxon ranges locally into our region: **Smooth Lip Fern : *Cheilánthes alabaménsis*** Kunze, 1847. (*The Fern Guide,* p. 186.) Differing in the blade being somewhat narrowed below and the pinnules being glabrous. Fla., "along Indian River," and Washington Co.; La., Orleans and Winn parishes. [S. upl., lower n. and w. states, and Mex.] Calcareous rocks, and invading shell mounds.

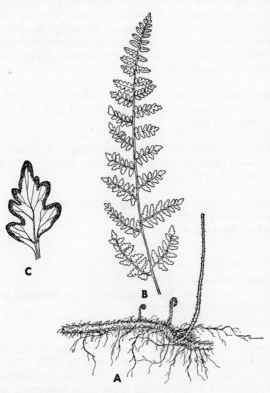

SOUTHERN LIP FERN : *Cheilanthes microphylla*

A. Rootstock.   B. Blade, reduced.   C. Pinnule.

Hairy Lip Fern : Cheilánthes lanòsa

FEATURES: Stipe *ca.* 8 to 15 cm. long, dark brown and copiously hairy, as is also the rachis. Blade dark green, *ca.* 10 to 20 cm. long and 3 to 6 broad, 2-pinnate. Pinnules cut into rounded-oblong segments, hairy, especially beneath. Sori rather sparse, the indusioid strips barely covering them. The fronds are able to withstand considerable drying out, reviving when moistened.

RANGE: From the Fall Line down to Coffee Co., Ga., and Hale Co., Ala.; disjunct in Natchitoches Par., La. [S. upl. and up to Conn. and Minn.]

HABITAT: On ledges and slopes of crumbling rocks, chiefly sandstone and shale, but locally other sorts, including limestone. Soil subacid or rarely circumneutral.

CULTURE: Though not especially striking, the adaptability of this fern to a variety of situations makes it desirable as a rock-garden subject.

NOMENCLATURE:

Cheilanthes lanosa D. C. Eaton, 1859. (S)
(*Nephrodium lanosum* Michaux, 1803, in part, basionym.)
Cheilanthes vestita Swartz, 1806.
(*Adiantum vestitum* Sprengel, 1804, basionym.)

Another member of the genus barely enters our region: Woolly Lip Fern : Cheilánthes tomentòsa Link, 1833. (*The Fern Guide,* p. 190.) This differs from the above in averaging longer, in the stipe and rachis bearing scales along with hairs, and in being 3-pinnate with round pinnulets, the marginal flaps of which cover the sori fully. Reported here only in Bibb Co., Ga., and Charleston Co., S.C. [S. uplands, up to W. Va., and out to Ariz. and Mex.] See Appendix.

The nomenclatorial confusion between these two taxa in *Gray's Manual,* ed. 8, 1950, was discussed in *The Fern Guide.* Most current fern workers consider this to have been unfortunate and unnecessary, and it is ignored here.

HAIRY LIP FERN : *Cheilanthes lanosa*

A. Plant, reduced.   B. Pinna.   C. Pinnule, enlarged.

CLIFF-BRAKES : *PELLAÈA*

A Greek word for dusky was adapted as a name for this genus by Link in 1841. It comprises smallish tufted rock ferns of rather firm membranous texture, mostly 2- or 3-pinnate, with the pinnae jointed to the rachis and tending to break off at maturity. The fertile fronds are larger than the sterile, with narrower and more pointed divisions. The sporangia lie in rows at vein-tips, protected by long indusioid scarious reflexed marginal strips.

Hairy Cliff-Brake : *Pellaèa atropurpùrea*

FEATURES: Rootstock tipped by copious grayish scales which age pale brown. Stipe *ca.* 8 to 15 cm. long, like the rachis brownish black and rough-hairy. Blade *ca.* 10 to 20 cm. long and 6 to 12 broad, when fully developed 3-pinnate at base and 2- upward.

RANGE: Rare and widely scattered in our region—Jackson–Washington cos., Fla., and one co. each in sw. Ga., c. Ala., n. La., and e. Tex. [S. upl., ne. and sw. states, and Mex.]

HABITAT: Limestone cliffs and ledges. Soil circumneutral.

CULTURE: Not cultivated in our region.

NOMENCLATURE:

Pellaea atropurpurea Link, 1841. (S)
(*Pteris atropurpurea* L., 1753, basionym.)

———————

Various tropical species are occasionally grown in Fla. gardens, and one native of Africa is reported as an escape in the lower peninsula: *Pellaèa víridis* Prantl, 1882. This differs from the above in being soft-scaly, with more widely spaced, rounder pinnulets.

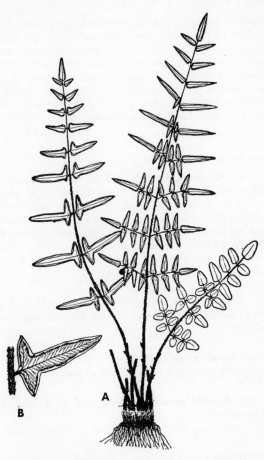

HAIRY CLIFF-BRAKE : *Pellaea atropurpurea*

A. Plant, reduced. B. Pinnule, enlarged.

BRAKES : *PTÉRIS*

Originally signifying a wing, the Greek word *pteris* came to be applied to ferns, and was taken up as a genus name by Linnaeus in 1753. Only three of its numerous species seem to be native in our region, but several from other lands have been introduced. The genus is characterized by having a simple vascular system, the veins being free or partially areolate, and by the sporangia being borne in a long strip under a reflexed indusioid margin. The basal chromosome number is 29.

Chinese Brake : *Ptéris vittàta*

FEATURES: Rootstock stoutish and knobby, copiously scaly, sending up tufted erect or spreading fronds. Stipe soft-scaly, *ca.* 5 to 10 cm. long. Blade *ca.* 25 to 50 cm. long and 13 to 25 broad, fine-scaly on rachis and on veins beneath, the scales on falling leaving the surfaces smooth. Pinnae firmly attached to rachis, truncate and scarcely auricled at base, the sterile ones callous-serrate, the lower relatively short and broad.

RANGE: Scattered over Fla., up to Charleston, S.C., and out to New Orleans, La. [Native of e. Asia, but escaping in many lands.]

HABITAT: Invading not only masonry and waste ground, but also seemingly natural rocky woodland and pineland.

CULTURE: Readily grown and long used as a mild-climate garden plant.

NOMENCLATURE:

Pteris vittata L., 1753.
Pycnodoria vittata Small, 1932. (S)

Hybrids between this introduced taxon and the native one treated next are not infrequent, combining the parental features in complex pattern.

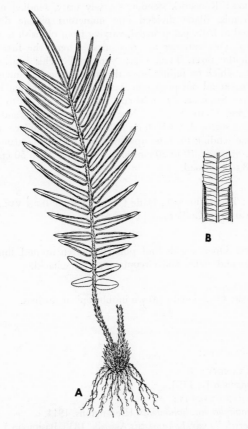

CHINESE BRAKE : *Pteris vittata*

A. Plant, reduced.   B. Section of fertile pinna.

Plumy Brake : *Ptéris longifòlia*

FEATURES: Rootstock slender, sparsely scaly, sending up tufts of fronds. Blade divided into numerous pinnae distinctly jointed at base, pale-fringed, varying from obtusish to acutish at tip. Two varieties are recognizable here, the first-named much the rarer. TYPE VAR.: Stipe and rachis bearing firm scales, which on falling leave the surface rough. Pinnae tending to extend out perpendicular to rachis, somewhat cordate at base. Stipe *ca.* 20 to 40 cm. long. Blade *ca.* 38 to 75 cm. long and 15 to 30 broad. NORTHERN VAR.: Stipe and rachis bearing soft scales, which on falling leave the surface smooth. Pinnae tending to slope upward from the rachis, truncate at base. Stipe *ca.* 10 to 20 cm. long. Blade *ca.* 25 to 50 cm. long and 8 to 15 broad.

RANGE: Fla., TYPE VAR., Dade Co. only; NORTHERN VAR., up to Broward and Collier cos. [Trop. Amer.]

HABITAT: Open woods and pineland, often around limestone ledges and sinks. Soil circumneutral to subacid.

CULTURE: Occasionally grown in subtropical gardens.

NOMENCLATURE:

TYPE VARIETY:
Pteris longifolia L., 1753.
NORTHERN VARIETY:
Pteris longifolia var. *bahaménsis* Hieronymus, 1914.
(*P. diversifolia* var. *bahamensis* Agardh, 1839, basionym.)
P. bahamensis Fée, 1852.
Pycnodoria pinetorum Small, 1918.
Pycnodoria bahamensis Small, 1938. (S)

The genus name used by Small for this and other species, *Pycnodoria,* was proposed by Presl in 1851, but is not now generally accepted.

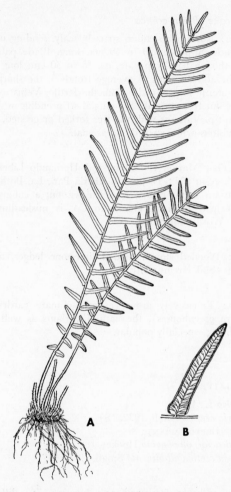

PLUMY BRAKE : *Pteris longifolia* v. *bahamensis*
A. Plant, reduced. B. Fertile pinna.

Cretan Brake : *Ptéris crètica*

FEATURES: Rootstock slender, sparsely scaly, sending up close-set fronds. Stipe *ca.* 20 to 40 cm. long. Blade palmate in aspect though basally pedate, *ca.* 15 to 30 cm. long and 13 to 25 broad. Divisions of average fronds 5, the sharply fine-serrate sterile ones broader than the fertile. Veins extending straight out from midrib. Sporangial strip ending well below division-tip. Variants with the tips forked or crested, or with the divisions white-striped, occasional.

RANGE: Fla., Marion–Columbia and Hernando–Liberty cos.; found here in 1838. Disjunct in Iberia Par., La. Both normal and variant forms escape from cultivation; a colony of the white-striped form in Hernando Co. is misleadingly luxuriant. [World subtropics.]

HABITAT: Wooded slopes, shaded limestone ledges, and sink margins. Soil circumneutral.

CULTURE: Extensively grown in mild-climate gardens (and northern greenhouses), the natural variants as well as cultivars being especially popular.

NOMENCLATURE:

Pteris cretica L., 1767.
Pycnodoria cretica Small, 1932. (S)
    WHITE-STRIPED VARIANT:
Ptéris crètica var. albolineàta Hooker, 1860.
Pycnodoria cretica albolineata Small, 1938. (S)

The Sword-brake, *Ptéris ensifòrmis* Burman, 1768, differs from the above in being larger and having major divisions round-lobed below; its white-striped variant, named **var. victòriae** by Baker, 1890, has escaped from cultivation into rocky woods in peninsular Florida, so remote from gardens as to give the impression of a native plant, although it actually came from India.

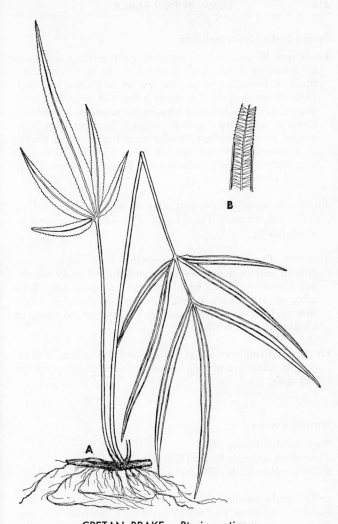

CRETAN BRAKE : *Pteris cretica*

A. Plant, reduced. B. Section of fertile pinna.

Spider Brake : *Ptéris multifida*

FEATURES: Rootstock short, copiously scaly, sending out close-set spreading fronds. Stipe smooth, *ca.* 10 to 20 cm. long. Blade outline oblong-triangular, *ca.* 18 to 35 cm. long and 13 to 25 broad, divided pedately below and pinnately above into *ca.* 5 or 7 well-spaced long narrow segments, the midrib between these rather broadly winged. Margins irregularly serrate. Sterile divisions broader than fertile. Veins simple or once-forked, sloping upward from midvein. Sporangial strip extending nearly to division-tip. Forms with segment tip crested occasional.

RANGE: Scattered over n. pen. Fla., up to New Hanover Co., N.C., and out to c. Tex. [Native of e. Asia, but escaped in many lands.]

HABITAT: Escaped into damp crevices in masonry, waste ground, and even into seemingly undisturbed rocky woods. Soil circumneutral. In addition to the colloquial name here taken up, it is locally known as "Huguenot Fern," in reference to its having been found in a Huguenot cemetery in Charleston, S.C., in 1868.

CULTURE: Readily grown and much used in southern gardens (and northern greenhouses), tending to spread by spores far and wide.

NOMENCLATURE:

Pteris multifida Poiret, 1804.
Pycnodoria multifida Small, 1938. (S)
Pteris serrulata L., Jr., 1781, not valid.

The use by Small of the genus name *Pycnodoria* for this and the three preceding species was based on a viewpoint not generally accepted, that since Bracken was native to the region where Linnaeus lived, he must have based the name *Pteris* on that. From a study of his writings, however, Christensen found that he based it primarily on taxon *longifolia,* and this view is favored here.

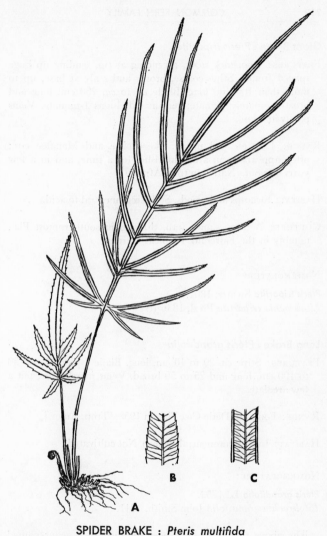

SPIDER BRAKE : *Pteris multifida*

A. Plant, reduced.   Sections of B. Sterile and
C. Fertile pinnae.

Giant Brake : *Ptéris tripartìta*

FEATURES: Rootstock stout, ascending at tip, sending up huge spaced fronds. Stipe coarse, brown and scaly at base, up to more than 100 cm. long. Blade up to *ca.* 200 cm. long and broad, ternately pinnate; terminal divisions 1-pinnate. Veins partly areolate.

RANGE: Fla., escaped up to Okeechobee and Manatee cos.; often appears in an area, flourishes for a time, and in a few years dies out. [Native in trop. Africa.]

HABITAT: Swamps and woods. Soil circumneutral to acid.

CULTURE: A large showy fern, thriving in southernmost Fla., notably in the Fairchild Tropical Garden.

NOMENCLATURE:

Pteris tripartita Swartz, 1801.
Litobrochia tripartita Presl, 1836 (S)

Long Brake : *Ptéris grandifòlia*

FEATURES: Stipe *ca.* 20 to 40 cm. long. Blade 1-pinnate, *ca.* 50 to 100 cm. long and 25 to 50 broad. Veins mostly free, but a few areolate.

RANGE: Found in Dade Co., Fla., in 1950. [Trop. Amer.]

HABITAT: In a circumneutral swamp. Not cultivated.

NOMENCLATURE:

Pteris grandifolia L., 1753.
Litobrochia grandifolia John Smith, 1841.

The above two ferns have been assigned to a genus named *Litobrochia* by Presl in 1836, on the basis of the presence of areolate veins; this feature is not regarded as of generic significance by the leading present-day authorities, however, so they are here retained in *Pteris*.

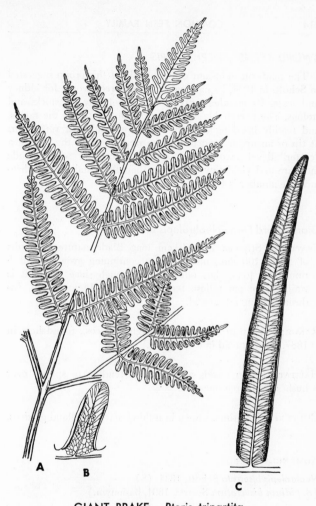

GIANT BRAKE : *Pteris tripartita*

A. Portions of frond, much reduced.   B. Fertile segment.

TALL BRAKE : *Pteris grandifolia*

C. Fertile pinna.

SWORD FERNS : *NEPHRÓLEPIS*

The reniform indusium characteristic of this group suggested to Schott, in 1834, its naming from the Greek words for kidney and scale. Its members spread into colonies by rootstocks and stolons. The narrow blade has the pinnae jointed to the rachis, and readily breaking off. The veins fork and bear round sori at tip of an upper branch. On the upper side of the pinnae a "crater" develops over each sorus, the cells of which exude moisture and yield tiny calcium carbonate crystals. Basal chromosome number is 41.

Giant Sword Fern : *Nephrólepis biserràta*

FEATURES: Stipe *ca.* 20 to 40 cm. long. Blade mature at lengths of 50 to 100 cm., but at times continuing growth until 5 times this long, thus our longest, though since its habit is trailing, not our tallest, fern; breadth *ca.* 15 to 30 cm. Indusia opening all around.

RANGE: Fla. up to Broward and Highlands cos.; found here in 1887. [Widespread in trop. Amer.]

HABITAT: Damp woods and thickets, tending to sprawl over bushes. Soil circumneutral.

CULTURE: Sometimes grown in mild-climate woodland gardens.

NOMENCLATURE:

Nephrolepis biserrata Schott, 1834. (S)
(*Aspidium biserratum* Swartz, 1801, basionym.)

Toothed Sword Fern : *Nephrólepis pectinàta* Schott, 1834.

This species resembles the Tuber Sword Fern treated on the following text-page, but is more graceful, thinner-textured with more prominent veins, and less winter-hardy. It has recently been found in a swamp in Collier Co., Fla. [Trop. Amer.]

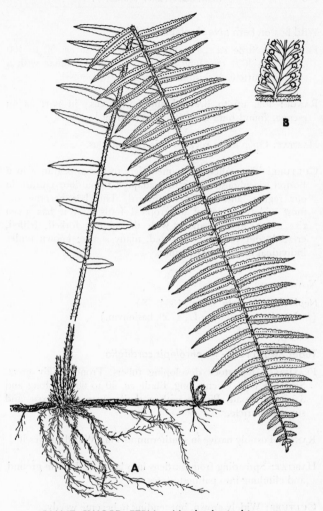

GIANT SWORD FERN : *Nephrolepis biserrata*

A. Plant, much reduced.   B. Section of fertile pinna.

Wild Boston Fern : *Nephrólepis exaltàta*

FEATURES: Stipe *ca.* 20 to 40 cm. long. Blade *ca.* 50 to 100 (rarely to 200) cm. long and 8 to 15 broad. Pinnae with a superior auricle. Indusium opening upward.

RANGE: Fla. up to Brevard and Citrus cos., in part as an escape; found here in 1859. [Trop. Amer.]

HABITAT: Open moist rocky woods. Soil various.

CULTURE: The colloquial name refers to the appearance in a Boston greenhouse of a strain adapted to outdoor culture in our region, and indoor northward. This has become the most widely grown of all tropical ferns, and it has given rise to a series of sports with the pinnae forked, frilled, crested, and variously dissected, many sterile; known under individual horticultural names.

NOMENCLATURE:

Nephrolepis exaltata Schott, 1834. (S)
(*Polypodium exaltatum* L., 1759, basionym.)

Tuber Sword Fern : *Nephrólepis cordifòlia*

FEATURES: Rootstock developing tubers. Fronds stiffly erect. Stipe *ca.* 8 to 15 cm. long. Blade *ca.* 30 to 60 cm. long and 3.5 to 7 broad. Pinnae with a shallowly cordate base and superior auricle.

RANGE: Possibly native in southernmost Fla. [World tropics.]

HABITAT: Spreading from gardens into lawns and waste ground, and climbing into palmetto trees.

CULTURE: Widely grown, but tending to become weedy.

NOMENCLATURE:

Nephrolepis cordifolia Presl, 1836. (S)
(*Polypodium cordifolium* L., 1753, basionym.)

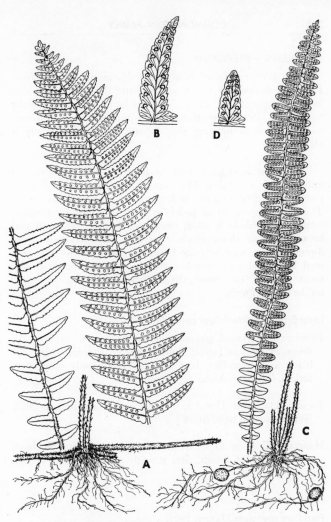

WILD BOSTON FERN : *Nephrolepis exaltata*

A. Rootstock and parts of blade.   B. Fertile pinna.

TUBER SWORD FERN : *Nephrolepis cordifolia*

C. Rootstock and blade.   D. Fertile pinna.

BRACKENS : *PTERÍDIUM*

While Linnaeus failed to separate this group of ferns from *Pteris,* its distinctness was recognized and the name, signifying in Greek resembling *Pteris,* was published (confusedly) by Scopoli in 1760. (The reference to Kuhn in *The Fern Guide* was intended to indicate that he was the first to apply it clearly.)

This genus is characterized by its parts bearing hairs, but unlike *Pteris* no scales. The rootstock is cord-like and long-creeping, sending up a row of huge coarse but deciduous fronds. The woody stipe is *ca.* 25 to 50 cm. long, with multiple vascular strands. The blade is about equal to the stipe in length and breadth (or at times much elongated) and ternately 2- to 3-pinnate. The sporangia are borne on a heavy cross-vein, covered by a real indusium beneath the reflexed indusioid segment margin. The basal chromosome number is 52, quite unlike that of *Pteris.*

Lacy Bracken : *Pterídium caudàtum*

FEATURES: Terminal pinnule-segment *ca.* 3 to 6 cm. long, 12 times as long as broad; inner segments spaced, giving the blade a skeleton-like, lacy aspect. Veins mostly only once-forked. Tissue glabrous or essentially so.

RANGE: Fla. up to Duval and Citrus cos.; found here in 1838. [Widespread in trop. Amer.]

HABITAT: Tending to form thickets in barrens, dry pineland, and margins of woods. Soil strongly acid to circumneutral. Not cultivated.

NOMENCLATURE:

Pteridium caudatum Maxon, 1901.
(*Pteris caudata* L., 1753, basionym.) (S)
Pteridium aquilinum var. *caudatum* Sadebeck, 1897.

While in a world-wide sense this taxon may be only varietally distinct, in our region it shows no intergradation, so is here treated as a species.

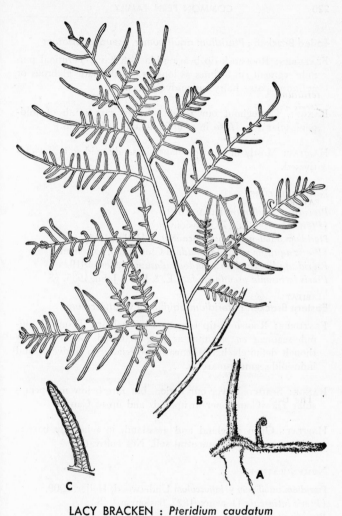

LACY BRACKEN : *Pteridium caudatum*

A. Rootstock.   B. Portion of blade, reduced.
C. Fertile segment.

Tailed Bracken : *Pterídium aquilìnum* v. *pseudocaudàtum*

FEATURES: Rootstock-tip bearing blackish hairs. Terminal pinnule segment *ca.* 8 times as long as broad. Blade glabrous or
at most sparse hairy on midveins beneath.

RANGE: Throughout our region, though rare south of mid-
peninsular Fla. [Also in s. uplands and n. lowlands.]

HABITAT: Mostly in open pineland, in sandy acid soil. Not cultivated.

NOMENCLATURE:

Pteridium aquilinum Kuhn, 1879.
(*Pteris aquilina* L., 1753, basionym.)
Pteridium aquilinum v. pseudocaudatum Heller, 1900.
(*Pteris aquilina* v. *pseudocaudata* Clute 1900, basionym.)
Pteridium latiusculum pseudocaudatum Maxon, 1919.
Pteris latiuscula pseudocaudata E. & R. St. John, 1935. (S)

Eastern Bracken : *Pterídium aquilìnum* v. *latiúsculum*

FEATURES: Rootstock-tip bearing whitish hairs. Terminal pinnule-segment *ca.* 4 times as long as broad. Blade variably
though definitely hairy beneath, especially on midveins and
indusioid segment-margins.

RANGE: Scattered over our region, but rare below mid-peninsular Fla. [Commoner in uplands and up to Can.]

HABITAT: Open pineland and grassland, in relatively barren,
acid or rarely circumneutral soil. Not cultivated.

NOMENCLATURE:

Pteridium aquilinum v. latiusculum Underwood; Heller, 1909.
(*Pteris latiuscula* Desvaux, 1827, basionym.) (S)
Pteridium latiusculum Hieronymus, 1914.

The two taxa treated on this page not only intergrade with
one another, but also seem to differ only in minor respects
from the original taxon to which the epithet *aquilinum* was
applied, so are classed as varieties of it.

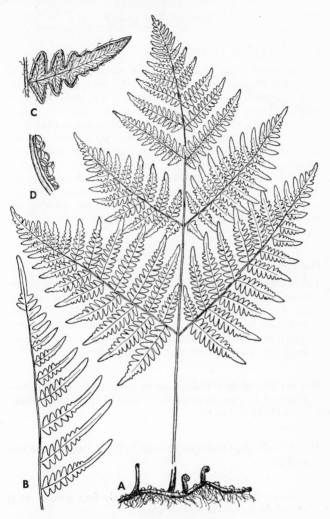

EASTERN BRACKEN : *Pteridium aquilinum* v. *latiusculum*
A. Plant, reduced. C. Pinnule and D. Soral strip.

TAILED BRACKEN : *Pt. a.* v. *pseudocaudatum*
B. Pinna-tip.

FLAKELET FERNS : *HYPÓLEPIS*

This genus name, from the Greek words for beneath and scale, was proposed by Bernhardi in 1806 for a group of ferns with marginal sori lacking an indusium, but protected by a reflexed flap of blade-tissue. The rootstock is rope-like, extensively creeping, clothed with hair-like scales, and sending up a row of large fronds. The blade is multiply pinnate and the veins are free. The sori are borne at vein-tip close to pinnulet margins and covered by a gray scale-like marginal extension. This resembles that of the Maidenhair Ferns (*Adiantum*), but differs in not bearing the sori on its inner surface. There are a number of species in the world tropics, one entering our region. The basal chromosome number is 52.

Flakelet Fern : *Hypólepis règens*

FEATURES: Rootstock-hairs fine, matted. Stipe *ca.* 20 to 40 cm. long, brown, prickly, as is also the rachis. Blade at maturity *ca.* 40 to 80 cm. long and broad (locally larger), 3- or 4-pinnate. Tissue thinnish, pale beneath, somewhat glandular-pubescent. Pinnulets cut into crenate lobes; sori developing singly on upper margin near base of a lobe-sinus.

RANGE: Fla. in three disjunct areas, Monroe Co., Okeechobee–Clay and Pinellas–Hernando cos.; found here in 1895. [Widespread in trop. Amer.]

HABITAT: Swamps and damp woods. Soil circumneutral to sub-acid.

CULTURE: Suitable only for a large-scale fern garden, as it spreads by rootstocks far and wide.

NOMENCLATURE:

Hypolepis repens Presl, 1836. (S)
(*Lonchitis repens* L., 1753, basionym.)

FLAKELET FERN : *Hypolepis repens*

A. Portions of frond, much reduced.   B. Fertile pinnule.

WEDGELET FERNS : *SPHENÓMERIS*

This genus name, from Greek words for wedge and division, was proposed by Maxon in 1913 for a group of ferns which had been shifted around by previous workers to at least 6 different genera. They are regarded as primitive in that the sori are borne at division-tip. About 15 species are known in the world tropics, one reaching Florida.

The creeping rootstock sends up close-set fronds. The blade is divided into multiple wedge-shaped segments. On sterile ones the veins are enlarged at tip and end below shallow notches; on fertile, sori arise from a group of 2 or 3 veins, and are protected by a flattened cornucopia-like indusium. The basal chromosome number of our species is 29.

Wedgelet Fern : *Sphenómeris clavàta*

FEATURES: Stipe slender, smooth, bronzy below, *ca.* 10 to 20 cm. long. Blade pale green, *ca.* 15 to 30 cm. long and 6 to 12 broad, divided in somewhat zigzag pattern into numerous spaced narrowly wedge-shaped segments *ca.* 1 to 2 cm. long. On dry rocks may be much reduced.

RANGE: Dade and Monroe cos., Fla.; found here in 1903. [Widespread in W.I.]

HABITAT: Limestone ledges, cliffs, and sink walls, in open pineland and woodland. Soil circumneutral.

CULTURE: Worth trying in a subtropical rock garden.

NOMENCLATURE:

Sphenomeris clavata Maxon, 1913. (S)
(*Adiantum clavatum* L., 1753, basionym.)
Davallia clavata J. E. Smith, 1793.
Stenoloma clavatum Fée, 1852.
Lindsaea clavata Mettenius, 1861.
Odontosoria clavata John Smith, 1875.
Schizoloma clavata Kuhn, 1882.

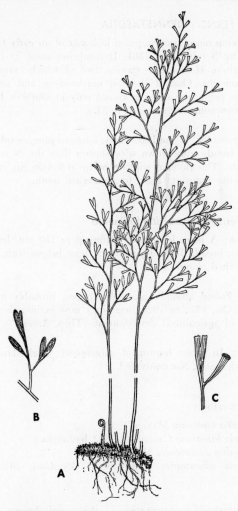

WEDGELET FERN : *Sphenomeris clavata*

A. Plant. B. Sterile and C. Fertile pinnules, enlarged.

CUPLET FERNS : *DENNSTAÈDTIA*

This genus name was proposed in honor of an early German botanist by Bernhardi in 1801. It comprises some 75 tropical and Southern Hemisphere species, two of which extend into North America. One of these is northeastern and southern-upland in range, the other is known only in southern Florida. Basal chromosome number is 32 to 34.

The rootstock is cord-like and long-creeping, sending up close-set fronds with brown stipe shorter than the 2- to 3-pinnate blade. The globular sori are borne at a vein tip, enclosed in a cup-like indusium fused to a marginal tooth.

Cuplet Fern : *Dennstaèdtia bipinnàta*

FEATURES: A huge fern, with blade up to 150 cm. long and 100 cm. broad. Blade 3-pinnate, at least below, with numerous toothed pinnulets.

RANGE: Found around Lake Okeechobee, probably in Palm Beach Co., Fla., in 1926; seemingly now extinct there as a result of agricultural development. [Trop. Amer.]

HABITAT: In moist humus of subtropical jungle land. Soil somewhat acid. Not cultivated.

NOMENCLATURE:

Dennstaedtia bipinnata Maxon, 1938.
(*Dicksonia bipinnata* Cavanilles, 1802, basionym.)
Dennstaedtia adiantoides Moore, 1857. (S)
(*Dicksonia adiantoides* Humboldt & Bonpland, 1810, basionym.)

The northern representative of the genus, known as **Hay Scented Fern**, *Dennstaèdtia punctilòbula* Moore, 1857, was treated in *The Fern Guide,* p. 192. It ranges southward sparingly into the N.C. Piedmont and lower mountains out to Ark., but scarcely enters our region. See Appendix.

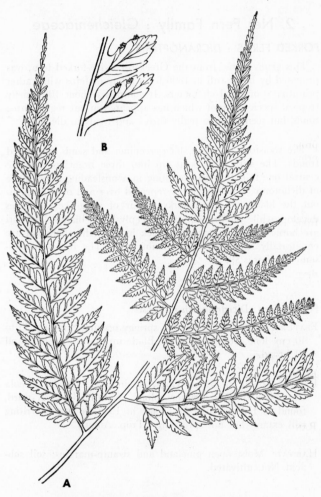

CUPLET FERN : *Dennstaedtia bipinnata*

A. Portions of blade, reduced.   B. Fertile pinnules.

2. Net Fern Family : *Gleicheniàceae*

FORKED FERNS : *DICRANÓPTERIS*

This genus name, from the Greek for twice-forked fern, was proposed by Bernhardi in 1806 for a group of ferns with rather primitive sporangial characters. It comprises about 100 chiefly tropical species, one of which has appeared in our region three times, but seems not to really thrive and tends to die out.

The rootstock is coarse, long-creeping, and sends up spaced fronds. The stipe divides at tip into three branches, but the central one fails to grow, resulting in a misleading appearance of dichotomy; this behavior is repeated over and over throughout the blade. At lower forks a pair of wing-like structures develop, while the branches bear deeply lobed blades. The sori are borne near vein bases and lack indusia; the sporangia are equatorially surrounded by annulus cells. The basal chromosome number is 39.

Forked Fern : *Dicranópteris flexuòsa*

FEATURES: Fronds of firm, dry, springy texture. Stipe *ca.* 20 to 40 cm. long, brown, glabrous. Blade up to 100 cm. long and 50 broad.

RANGE: Found in Mobile Co., Ala., in 1913, and in Osceola Co., Fla., in 1947, neither colony persisting long. A third, found in Hillsborough Co., Fla., in 1955, is at this writing still extant, but not spreading. [Trop. Amer.]

HABITAT: Moist open pineland and swamp-margins; soil sub-acid. Not cultivated.

NOMENCLATURE:

Dicranopteris flexuosa Underwood, 1907.
(*Mertensia flexuosa* Schrader, 1824, basionym.)
Gleichenia flexuosa Mettenius, 1863.

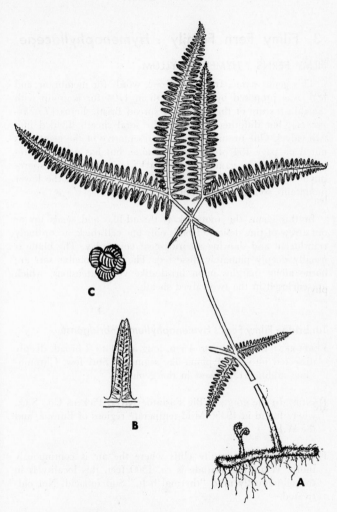

FORKED FERN : *Dicranopteris flexuosa*

A. Plant, reduced.   B. Pinna.   C. Sporangia, enlarged.

3. Filmy Fern Family : *Hymenophyllàceae*

FILMY FERNS : *HYMENOPHÝLLUM*

This genus name, from the Greek words for membrane and leaf, was proposed by J. E. Smith in 1794 for a group with the thin texture of the more widespread Bristle Ferns (*Trichomanes*), but differing in having the soral sheath divided into two valves. One presumed U.S. representative of the genus was noted on page 194 of *The Fern Guide,* but has now been reinterpreted as the gametophyte of a *Vittaria*. Recently a sporophyte which could be named has been discovered in the lower mountains, so is treated herein.

In this genus the rootstock is thread-like and sends up or out a row of tiny delicate fronds only one cell thick, accordingly translucent and showing an iridescent color play. The blade is usually deeply pinnately dissected. The tiny globular sori are borne along margins upon bristle-like vein extensions, which are enclosed in the two-valved sheath.

Tunbridge Filmy Fern : *Hymenophýllum tunbridgénsè*

FEATURES: Blade *ca.* 2 to 4 cm. long and 1 to 2 broad, deeply dissected into lobed pinna-like segments. Sori few. Chromosome number 13, lowest in the genus.

RANGE: In the gorge of Big Eastatoe River, Pickens Co., S.C., where found in 1935. [Mild-temperate regions of Europe, and the W.I.]

HABITAT: Shaded granite cliffs where the air is continuously moist. While the altitude is *ca.* 1500 feet, this locality is in the climatically mild "thermal belt." Soil subacid. Not cultivated.

NOMENCLATURE:

Hymenophyllum tunbridgense J. E. Smith, 1794, correction.
(*Trichomanes tunbrigense* L., 1753, basionym.)

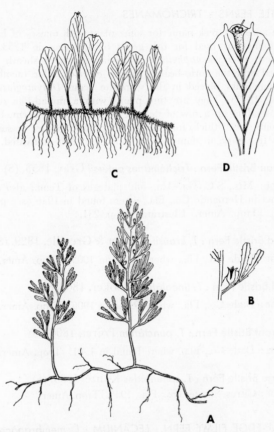

TUNBRIDGE FILMY FERN : *Hymenophyllum tunbridgense*

A. Plant. B. Fertile segment, enlarged.

PLATEAU BRISTLE FERN : *Trichomanes petersii*

C. Plant. B. Blade, enlarged.

BRISTLE FERNS : *TRICHÓMANES*

An ancient Greek name for some plant with masses of hair-like stems was used for this genus by Linnaeus in 1753. It differs from *Hymenophyllum* in having the soral sheath undivided and the sorus-bearing bristle exserted. Our members are sometimes placed in the segregate genus *Didymoglossum* (Presl, 1843). They are tiny plants with a thread-like rootstock sending up a row of delicate fronds *ca.* 1 to 2 cm. long and only 1 cell thick, forming mats on rocks, humus, or sometimes tree bark, in damp, shady situations. Not cultivated.

Plateau Bristle Fern : *Trichómanes petérsii* Gray, 1853. (S)

RANGE: Mts., S.C.–Ga.–Ala., and plateaus of Tenn.; also disjunct in Hernando Co., Fla., where found in 1936 (see page 29). [Trop. Amer.] Illustrated on p. 231.

Lobed Bristle Fern : *T. kraùsii* Hooker & Greville, 1829. (S)

RANGE: Dade Co., Fla., where found in 1903. [Trop. Amer.]

Lined Bristle Fern : *T. lineolàtum* Hooker, 1867. (S)

RANGE: Dade Co., Fla., where found in 1906. [Trop. Amer.]

Fragrant Bristle Fern : *T. punctàtum* Poiret, 1808. (S)

RANGE: Dade Co., Fla., where found in 1901. [Trop. Amer.]

Wedge Bristle Fern : *T. sphenoìdes* Kunze, 1835. (S)

RANGE: Citrus–Sumter cos., Fla.; 1936. [Trop. Amer.]

SCALE-EDGE FILMY FERN : *LECÀNIUM* : *L. membranàceum* Presl, 1843 (basionym *Trichomanes membranaceum* L., 1753)

This genus was named from a Greek word for dish by Presl in 1843. It is unique in the fronds being 2 cells thick and bearing paired marginal scales. The one species resembles *Trichomanes krausii*, but is larger and more irregular.

RANGE: Found in 1929 in acid humus of a wet meadow in Harrison Co., Miss. [Trop. Amer.]

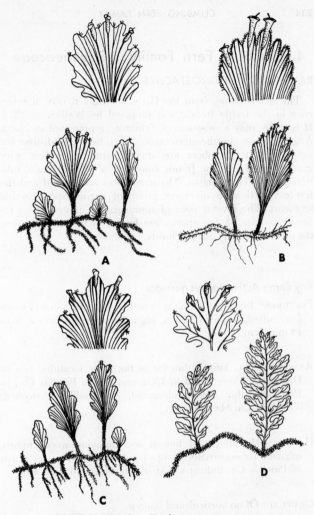

BRISTLE FERNS : *Trichomanes,* species

Plant and enlarged blade-tip of A. FRAGRANT, *T. punctatum.*

B. WEDGE, *T. sphenoides.*   C. LINED, *T. lineolatum.*

D. LOBED, *T. krausii.*

4. Climbing Fern Family : *Schizaeàceae*

RAY FERNS : *ACTINÓSTACHYS*

This genus name, from the Greek for stalked rays in reference to the fertile fronds, was proposed by Wallich in 1842. It is really only a subgenus of *Schizaea* (represented in North America by one northeastern taxon) but is here kept distinct for simplicity. Its members are small plants resembling wiry grasses or sedges. The fronds consist of a slender blade, subtriangular in cross-section. The sterile ones are pointed and the fertile tipped by a divergent group of narrow spore-bearing segments. The several rows of sporangia are protected by reflexed margins. A few species are known in tropical America, the present the only one in Florida.

Ray Fern : *Actinóstachys germáni*

FEATURES: Rootstock slender, tipped by a bristly tuber. Fronds few, tufted, *ca.* 6 to 12 cm. high. Fertile segments *ca.* 8 to 15 mm. long.

RANGE: S. Fla., known thus far at but three localities, two in Dade Co., where found in 1904, and one in Pinellas Co., in 1952. Probably more widespread, but readily overlooked. [On a few Caribbean islands.]

HABITAT: Hummocks of humus and decaying wood, mostly subacid. Its occurrence in open palmetto land as far north as Pinellas Co. indicates that it can withstand light frost.

CULTURE: Of no horticultural interest.

NOMENCLATURE:

Actinostachys germani Fée, 1866. (S)
Schizaea germani Prantl, 1881.

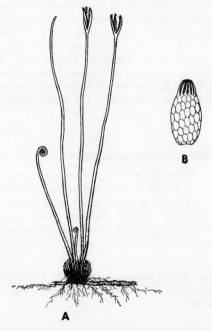

RAY FERN : *Actinostachys germani*
A. Plant. B. Sporangium, enlarged.

TWIN-SPORE-STALK FERNS : ANÈMIA

This curious genus name, proposed by Swartz in 1806, is derived from the Greek for without threads, perhaps in reference to the lack of a covering over the sporangia. The genus is characterized by a long erect stipe surmounted by a 1- to 3-pinnate triangular blade; on fertile fronds the lowest pair of pinnae are long-stalked and stand erect, bearing at tip clusters of sporangia in double rows on slender strips of laminar tissue. The presence of annulus cells at one end of the sporangium places the genus in the Climbing Fern Family. It is represented in the world tropics by a score of species, two of which range into the U.S.: one occurs in the region covered by this *Guide,* the other in west Texas. The basal chromosome number is 38.

Pineland Fern : Anèmia adiantifòlia

FEATURES: Rootstock creeping, brown-scaly. Stipe *ca.* 13 to 25 cm. long, brown at base and yellow upward, fine-hairy. Blade *ca.* 13 to 25 cm. long and 10 to 20 broad, in especially dry places much reduced. Division mostly 2-pinnate, with the pinnules deeply lobed, producing a lacy pattern. Veins numerous, 2- or 3-forked, free at tip.

RANGE: Fla., in two disjunct areas, Dade–Monroe–Collier cos., where found in 1838, and Citrus–Sumter cos., in 1934. [Caribbean lands.]

HABITAT: In pineland on sandy or limy flats, less commonly in woodland (there growing larger). Soil subacid to circumneutral.

CULTURE: Can be grown in a dry garden situation.

NOMENCLATURE:

Anemia adiantifolia Swartz, 1806. (S)
(*Osmunda adiantifolia* L., 1753, basionym.)

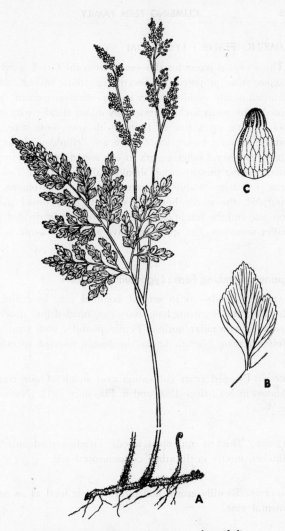

PINELAND FERN : *Anemia adiantifolia*

A. Plant of small form.   B. Pinnule, enlarged.
C. Sporangium, enlarged.

CLIMBING FERNS : *LYGÒDIUM*

The accepted name for this genus, from the Greek word for flexuous, was proposed by Swartz in 1801. Several others published nearly simultaneously are by common consent disregarded. The genus is characterized by a long slender wiry rootstock sending up a row of fronds with very short stipe and elongate twining rachis; since there are "climbing" ferns belonging to several other genera in our region (and the tropics generally) the present group should really be termed Twining Ferns, but long established usage prevails. The pinnae are dimorphic, the sterile lower ones forking into broad paired segments, and the fertile terminal more complexly divided into smaller segments. The sporangia have a terminal annulus.

Japanese Climbing Fern : *Lygòdium japónicum*

FEATURES: Blade up to several hundred cm. long and 30 broad. Pinna-segments long-triangular, divided into dissected pinnules of similar outline. Fertile pinnules with numerous lobes bearing beneath linear tip double rows of sporangia.

RANGE: Escaped from cultivation over much of our region; known in N.C. since 1900 and in Fla. since 1932. [Native of e. Asia.]

HABITAT: Thickets and open woods, invading road cuts and ditches, mostly in disturbed circumneutral soil.

CULTURE: Readily grown and rather widely used as an ornamental vine.

NOMENCLATURE:

Lygodium japonicum Swartz, 1801. (S)
(*Ophioglossum japonicum* Thunberg, 1784, basionym.)

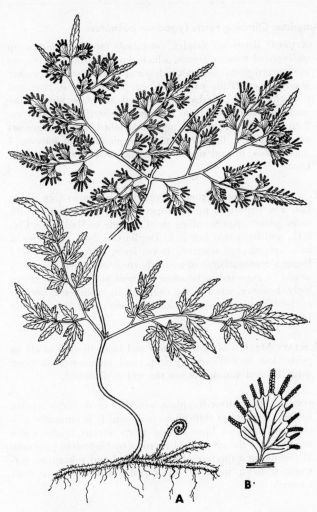

JAPANESE CLIMBING FERN : *Lygodium japonicum*

A. Base and tip of a plant. B. Fertile pinnule, enlarged.

American Climbing Fern : *Lygòdium palmàtum*

FEATURES: Rootstock slender, extensively creeping, sending up well-spaced twining fronds, which though seemingly delicate are evergreen at high altitudes and latitudes. Stipe rather short, brown. Blade pale green, *ca.* 50 to 100 cm. long and 8 to 15 broad, divided into spaced alternate pinnae, the stalks of which fork into 2 segments. Sterile segments *ca.* 3 to 6 cm. across, deeply palmately lobed. Fertile segments *ca.* 6 to 12 cm. long, 2-pinnate, the pinnules cut into *ca.* 3 linear lobes, toward tip of which the rows of sporangia are borne.

RANGE: Rare in our region. Reported from Lemon City, Dade Co., Fla. (although this is suspected of representing a cultivated plant). Known along the Fall Line in Darlington Co., S.C., and from that line e. to Duplin Co., N.C. [Widespread in s. uplands and scattered in ne. states up to *ca.* lat. 43°.] Being a representative of a chiefly tropical family, this taxon would be expected to be more frequent in our region. Seemingly, however, when in the course of its evolution it became cold-tolerant it also lost the ability to withstand high summer temperatures.

HABITAT: Margins of acid swamps and bogs, the soil sandy or peaty, low in ordinary nutrients, and intensely acid. Soon dwindles and vanishes when the soil is disturbed.

CULTURE: This attractive plant would be a desirable garden subject, were it not difficult to maintain. It is unusually sensitive to traces of lime and of heavy metals in the water supply, or to the invasion of its roots by burrowing creatures. If planted in a mixture of salt-free sand and sphagnum, surrounded by a moat or an impenetrable barrier, it may succeed.

NOMENCLATURE:

Lygodium palmatum Swartz, 1806. (S)
(*Gisopteris palmata* Bernhardi, 1801, basionym.)

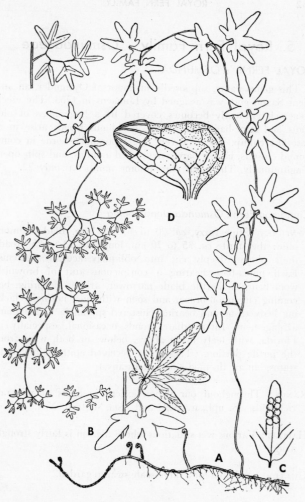

AMERICAN CLIMBING FERN : Lygodium palmatum

A. Plant, reduced. B. Sterile and C. Fertile divisions.

D. Sporangium, enlarged.

241

5. Royal Fern Family : *Osmundàceae*

ROYAL FERNS : *OSMÚNDA*

This genus name, supposedly in honor of Osmunder, an ancient Saxon god, was assigned by Linnaeus in 1753. The erect rootstock gradually becomes covered by a huge mass of old roots and stipe-bases. The large, deciduous fronds arise in a vase-like clump. The relatively large sporangia, borne in compound clusters, have a barely developed annulus, and split open longitudinally. The basal chromosome number is only 22.

Cinnamon Fern : *Osmúnda cinnamòmea*

FEATURES: Stipe fuzzy, *ca.* 20 to 40 cm. long. Blades dimorphic: the sterile *ca.* 35 to 70 cm. long and 13 to 25 broad, their pinnae deeply cut into obliquely acutish segments. Each pinna-base bearing a conspicuous tuft of brownish wool beneath. Fertile blade narrower, arising in spring, becoming cinnamon-brown and soon withering, normally lacking leafy tissue and bearing clustered sporangia in 2-pinnate arrangement. Intermediate fronds occasional, especially in Florida, with leafy tissue above, below, or both ways from the fertile portion. (These have received epithets in variety status, but are deemed not to merit any.)

RANGE: Throughout our region except in areas of mineral-rich soils. (S. upl., n. N.A. and Asia, subtrop. N.A.)

HABITAT: Various wet situations where the soil is fairly strongly acid.

CULTURE: Suitable for a large-scale swamp garden.

NOMENCLATURE:

Osmunda cinnamomea L., 1753. (S)

The other 1-pinnate member of the genus, *O. claytoniana* L., 1753, is northern and does not enter our region. See Appendix.

spores in center

CINNAMON FERN : *Osmunda cinnamomea*

A. Plant with fertile and sterile fronds, much reduced.
B. Sterile segments.   C. Group of sporangia, enlarged.

Royal Fern : *Osmúnda regàlis* var. *spectábilis*

FEATURES: Dissimilar in aspect from our other representative of the genus. Rootstock erect, becoming covered with old roots and stipe-bases, ultimately rising to form a short "trunk." Stipe *ca.* 30 to 60 cm. long, glabrous, grayish green or pink. Blade *ca.* 38 to 75 cm. long (or more in especially favorable spots) and 25 to 50 broad, 2-pinnate with spaced oblong pinnules, hairy on axes beneath. Dimorphism limited to blade-tip: in fertile fronds several pinnae there replaced by clusters of sporangia normally unaccompanied by leafy tissue. (Variants with anomalously-shaped pinnules or with admixtures of sterile and fertile portions have received unnecessary epithets.) In the species type, of northern Europe and Asia, fertile parts bear conspicuous narrow black scales, in the American variety these are sparse or lacking.

RANGE: Widespread over our region. [S. upl. (rare), n. N. Amer., trop. Amer.; related taxa in Europe and Asia.]

HABITAT: Swamps, bogs, and shallow waters. Soil varying from strongly acid to circumneutral, though in the latter the plants scarcely reproducing.

CULTURE: Ornamental and deserving use around the margins of garden pools, if of considerable size.

NOMENCLATURE:

SPECIES TYPE:
Osmunda regalis L., 1753. (S)
AMERICAN REPRESENTATIVE:
Osmunda regalis β L., 1753.
Osmunda regalis var. *spectabilis* Gray, 1858.
(*Osmunda spectabilis* Willdenow, 1810, basionym.)

A well-established industry in our region is the digging of Osmunda fiber (or "peat")—the old root and stipe tissue of these plants. This is extensively used in the culture of orchids and other epiphytes.

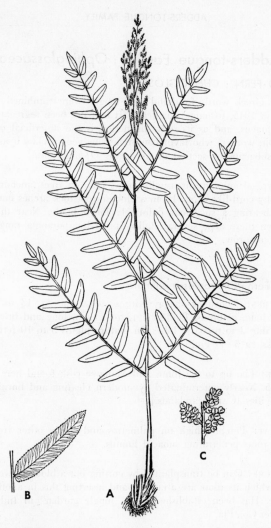

ROYAL FERN : *Osmunda regalis* v. *spectabilis*

A. Plant, much reduced.   B. Sterile pinnule.
C. Group of sporangia, enlarged.

6. Adders-tongue Family : *Ophioglossàceae*

HAND FERN : *CHEIROGLÓSSA*

The Greek words for hand and tongue were combined by Presl, in 1845, to name this genus. It had not been segregated by Linnaeus, and as its only distinction is the superficial one of habit, workers who favor comprehensive genera class it as a mere subgenus or section of his genus *Ophioglossum.*

A typical epiphyte, it usually grows high on trees, anchored by fleshy cord-like roots. From a globose rootstock arches out a stipe, bearing a succulent palmately lobed blade. Near their junction there arise several stalks tipped by sporangia ranged in a double row.

Hand Fern : *Cheiroglóssa palmàta*

FEATURES: Rootstock shaggy with scales. Stipe *ca.* 13 to 25 cm. long, glabrous. Blade *ca.* 13 to 25 cm. long and broad, cut into 3 to 6 coarse lobes. In mature plants 5 to 10 fertile stalks, *ca.* 3 to 6 cm. long.

RANGE: Fla. up to St. Johns and Manatee cos.; found here in 1875. Nearly exterminated by modern clearing and burning activities. [Caribbean lands.]

HABITAT: Perched high on palmettos and rarely other trees, the roots penetrating subacid humus.

CULTURE: Can be transplanted by cutting out a block of wood to which its roots are attached, and inserting this in another tree. Has been established in a "jungle garden" in Indian River Co., Fla.

NOMENCLATURE:

Cheiroglossa palmata Presl, 1845. (S)
(*Ophioglossum palmatum* L., 1753, basionym.)

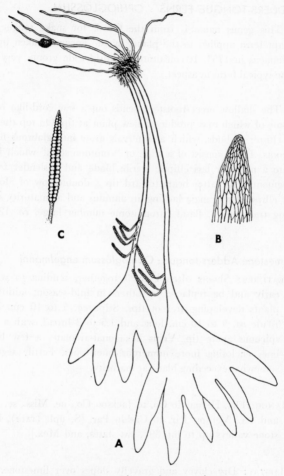

HAND FERN : *Cheiroglossa palmata*

A. Plant, reduced. B. Lobe-tip. C. Fertile spike.

ADDERS-TONGUE FERNS : *OPHIOGLÓSSUM*

This genus name is from the Greek for snake tongue, an inapt term applied to the plants by the ancients, taken up by Linnaeus in 1753. It constitutes a world-wide group, very unlike typical ferns in aspect.

The shallow erect rootstock sends out a few cord-like roots, some of which may produce a new plant at tip. On top there is a cluster of buds, which at intervals grow into glabrous fleshy shoots. These consist of a stipe or "common stalk" which forks into a more or less elliptic sterile blade and a slender fertile segment. The latter bears toward tip a double row of globose or ellipsoid sporangia lacking an annulus and at maturity splitting transversely. Basal chromosome number large, *ca.* 126.

Limestone Adders-tongue : *Ophioglóssum engelmánni*

FEATURES: Shoots often 2 or 3 together, tending to wither early and be replaced by others in mid-season; additional plants developing at root tips. Stipe *ca.* 5 to 10 cm. long. Blade *ca.* 5 to 10 cm. long and 1.5 to 3 broad, with a conspicuous acute tip. Veins hexagonal-areolate, a few heavy ones enclosing more numerous finer ones. Fertile segment somewhat exceeding blade at maturity.

RANGE: Fla., Hernando Co. to Jackson Co., ne. Miss., se. Ark., and La., Vernon Par. to Caddo Par. [S. upl. (rare), limestone valleys up to lat. 39°, sw. states, and Mex.]

HABITAT: Dry clayey and gravelly slopes over limestone. Soil circumneutral. Of no horticultural interest.

NOMENCLATURE:

Ophioglossum engelmanni Prantl, 1883. (S)

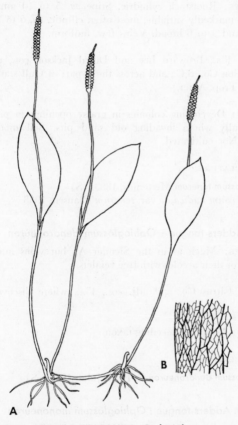

LIMESTONE ADDERS-TONGUE : *Ophioglossum engelmanni*
A. Group of plants.   B. Portion of blade, enlarged.

Slender Adders-tongue : *Ophioglóssum ténerum*

FEATURES: Rootstock cylindric. Stipe *ca.* 5 to 10 mm. long. Blade markedly variable, most often elliptic, *ca.* 5 to 10 mm. long and 3 to 6 broad. Veins few, uniform.

RANGE: Fla., Broward–Lee and Duval–Jackson cos., rare up to Dillon Co., S.C., and across the s. part of Gulf states to e. Tex. [Trop. Amer.]

HABITAT: Developing colonies in grassy openings in pineland, especially where invading old sand pits. Soil moderately acid. Not cultivated.

NOMENCLATURE:

Ophioglossum *tenerum* Mettenius, 1883. (S)
Ophioglossum nudicaule var. *tenerum* Clausen, 1938.

Veiny Adders-tongue : *Ophioglóssum dendroneùron*

FEATURES: Much as in the Slender A., but veins numerous, many of their areoles with free veinlets.

RANGE: Citrus Co. and adj. cos., Fla., where discovered in 1936.

HABITAT: As in the preceding taxon.

NOMENCLATURE:

Ophioglossum *dendroneuron* E. P. St. John, 1938. (S)

Mid-vein Adders-tongue : *Ophioglóssum mononeùron*

FEATURES: Rootstock subglobose. Blade round-ovate, *ca.* 3 to 6 mm. long and nearly as broad. One medial vein manifestly thickened toward blade-base.

RANGE and HABITAT: As in the preceding taxon.

NOMENCLATURE:

Ophioglossum *mononeuron* E. P. St. John, 1938. (S)

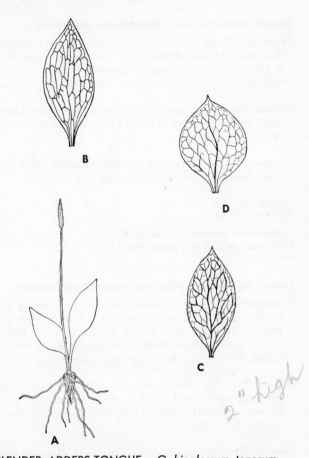

SLENDER ADDERS-TONGUE : *Ophioglossum tenerum*

A. Plant. B. Blade, enlarged.   VEINY ADDERS-TONGUE :
O. dendroneuron. C. Blade. MIDVEIN ADDERS-TONGUE :
O. mononeuron. D. Blade.

Stalked Adders-tongue : *Ophioglóssum petiolàtum*

FEATURES: Plants spreading into colonies by bud-tipped roots. Rootstock cylindric, sending up 1 to 5 fronds. Stipe *ca.* 4 to 8 cm. long. Blade abruptly expanded from a short stalk, tapering upward, *ca.* 2.5 to 5 cm. long and 1.5 to 3 broad.

RANGE: Fla., St. Johns Co. to Citrus Co., where found in 1935, northw.; rare up to Horry Co., S.C., and out to e. Tex. [World tropics.]

HABITAT: Grassy openings in pineland, invading roadsides and other disturbed ground. Soil various. Not cultivated.

NOMENCLATURE:

Ophioglossum petiolatum Hooker, 1823.
O. floridanum E. P. St. John, 1936. (S)

Tuber Adders-tongue : *Ophioglóssum crotalophoroìdes*

FEATURES: Rootstock a globose tuber up to a cm. in diam., sending up 1 to 3 fronds. TYPE VAR.: Stipe *ca.* 1 to 2 cm. long. Blade ovate, often folded, *ca.* 1.5 to 3 cm. long and 1 to 2 broad. DWARF VAR.: Dimensions *ca.* ⅓ the above values. Spike with a long bare tip.

RANGE: TYPE VAR.: Fla., Putnam Co. to Manatee Co., northw., sparingly up to Berkeley Co., S.C., and out to c. Tex. DWARF VAR.: Citrus–Sumter cos., Fla.; disjunct in Washington Co., Ala. [Trop. Amer.]

HABITAT: Meadows, grassy slopes, and, rarely, disturbed ground. Soil circumneutral. Not cultivated.

NOMENCLATURE:

Ophioglossum crotalophoroides Walter, 1788. (S)
    DWARF VARIETY:
O. crotalophoroides var. *nanum* Osten *ex* de Lichtenstein, 1944. (S, illustrated but not named)

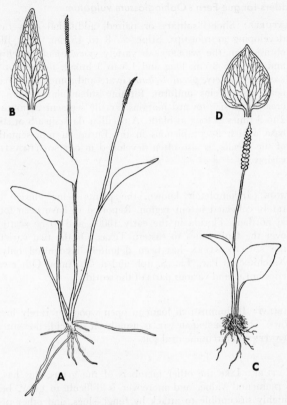

STALKED ADDERS-TONGUE : *Ophioglossum petiolatum*

A. Plant, reduced.   B. Blade.

TUBER ADDERS-TONGUE : *O. crotalophoroides*

C. Plant.   D. Blade, enlarged.

Adders-tongue Fern : Ophioglóssum vulgàtum

FEATURES: Shoots solitary or paired, additional ones rarely developing at root-tips. Stipe *ca.* 8 to 15 cm. long. Blade obtusish, in the WIDESPREAD variety, *pseudópodum,* elliptic and *ca.* 4 to 8 cm. long and 1.5 to 3 broad; in the SOUTH-EASTERN variety, *pycnóstichum,* ovate and somewhat broader near base. Veins uniform, forming subangular areoles decreasing in size toward margins. Fertile segment at maturity 2 to 3 times as long as blade. A peculiar dark sheath at stipe-base, which is conspicuous in the European representatives of the species, is also often developed in our SOUTHEASTERN variety.

RANGE: Incompletely known, the plants being elusive and rarely collected in our region. Reported to have been found in northern Florida in the early 1800s, and to be scattered over the Gulf states to eastern Texas. Of the two varieties, the SOUTHEASTERN has been definitely recognized only in Natchitoches Par., La. [S. upl. and n. N. Amer. Other varieties in Eu. and various parts of the world.]

HABITAT: In humus-rich loam in open woods or rarely meadows. The WIDESPREAD var. is usually in subacid, the SOUTH-EASTERN in circumneutral soil.

CULTURE: Like the other members of the genus, this has no ornamental value, and moreover is difficult to grow, being highly susceptible to attack by fungi, slugs, and other pests.

NOMENCLATURE:

SPECIES TYPE:
Ophioglossum vulgatum L., 1753. (S)
WIDESPREAD VARIETY:
O. vulgatum var. pseudopodum Farwell, 1916.
(*O. vulgatum* f. *pseudopodum* Blake, 1913, basionym.)
SOUTHEASTERN VARIETY:
O. vulgatum var. pycnostichum Fernald, 1939.

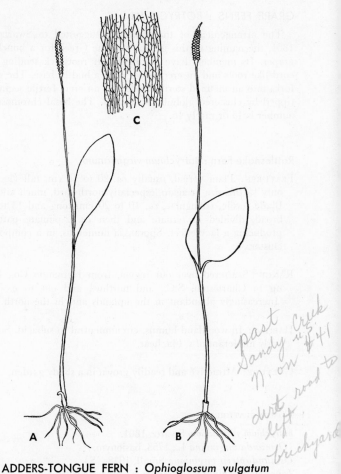

past Creek
Sandy "5
N. on #41
dirt road to
left.
brickyard

ADDERS-TONGUE FERN : *Ophioglossum vulgatum*

Plants of: A. Widespread and B. Southeastern varieties,
reduced. C. Portion of blade.

GRAPE FERNS : *BOTRÝCHIUM*

The arrangement of the sporangia suggested to Swartz, in 1801, the naming of this genus from the Greek for a bunch of grapes. Its members have a subglobular rootstock sending out cord-like roots and an erect shoot with a bud at base. The stipe forks into an inclined sterile blade and an erect fertile segment, tipped by clustered globular sporangia. The basal chromosome number is 45 or rarely 46.

Rattlesnake Fern : *Botrýchium virginiànum*

FEATURES: Plant vernal, usually *ca.* 20 to 40 cm. tall (locally only ½ this size or again, especially northward, much taller). Blade sessile, triangular, *ca.* 10 to 20 cm. long and 13 to 25 broad, divided in ternate and then *ca.* 2-pinnate pattern, producing a lacy effect. Sporangia numerous, in a compound cluster.

RANGE: Scattered over our region, from Hernando Co., Fla., up to Charleston, S.C., and northw., and out to e. Tex. [Increasingly abundant in the uplands and in the north.]

HABITAT: In woodland humus, circumneutral to subacid. Seemingly intolerant of s. Fla. heat.

CULTURE: Attractive and readily grown in a shady garden.

NOMENCLATURE:

Botrychium virginianum Swartz, 1801.
(*Osmunda virginiana* L., 1753, basionym.)
Osmundopteris virginiana Small, 1938. (S)
Japanobotrychium virginianum Nishida, 1958.

Since this differs from our other Grape Ferns in texture, veining, bud position, etc., and has 46 instead of 45 chromosomes, it is sometimes placed in a separate genus, the earliest name for which is *Japanobotrychium,* Masamune, 1931. This is not, however, widely accepted.

RATTLESNAKE FERN : Botrychium virginianum

A. Plant, reduced.

Alabama Grape Fern : *Botrýchium × alabaménsè*

FEATURES: Plant evergreen, fruiting in summer. Stipe *ca.* 2.5 to 5 cm. and blade-stalk 5 to 10 cm. long. Blade broad-triangular, *ca.* 8 to 15 cm. long and 10 to 20 broad, *ca.* 3-pinnately divided into wide-spaced roundish fine-toothed pinnulets.

RANGE: Widely scattered, Duval Co., Fla., to upland N.C. and S.C., and out to Mobile, Ala. (whence described), and George Co., Miss.; actually first collected in Ga., 1900.

HABITAT: Loamy soil, usually subacid, on wooded slopes, also invading old fields. Not cultivated.

NOMENCLATURE:

Botrychium [×] *alabamense* Maxon, 1906. (S)
B. biternatum × *lunarioides,* suggested by W. H. Wagner, 1960.

Prostrate Grape Fern : *Botrýchium lunarioìdes*

FEATURES: Plant subevergreen, fruiting in spring. Stipe very short; blade-stalk *ca.* 1.5 to 3 cm. long. Blade nearly prostrate, *ca.* 2.5 to 5 cm. long and 3 to 6 broad, ternately and then pinnately divided into close-set roundish coarse-toothed pinnulets.

RANGE: Widely disjunct, from Jefferson Co., Fla., to Charleston, S.C., where discovered in 1800, Richmond Co., S.C., and Mobile Co., Ala. (N.C., La. ?).

HABITAT: In rather dry situations, open woods on sandy slopes, invading old fields. Soil subacid. Not cult'd.

NOMENCLATURE:

Botrychium lunaroides Swartz, 1806; *lunarioides* Schkuhr, 1809.
(*Botrypus lunaroides* Michaux, 1803, basionym.)
Botrychium biternatum Underwood, 1896, misinterpretation.

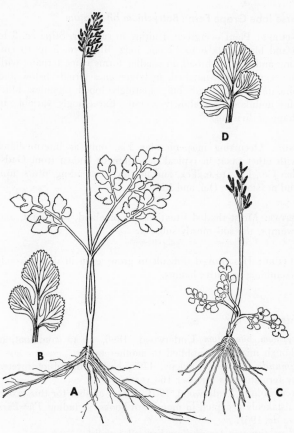

ALABAMA GRAPE FERN : *Botrychium alabamense*

A. Plant, reduced. B. Terminal segments.

PROSTRATE GRAPE FERN : *B. lunarioides*

C. Plant. D. Terminal segments.

Sparse-lobe Grape Fern : *Botrýchium biternàtum*

FEATURES: Plant evergreen, fruiting in summer. Stipe *ca.* 3 to 6 and blade-stalk 6 to 12 cm. long. Blade *ca.* 5 to 10 cm. long and 8 to 15 broad, in smaller forms twice ternate, with the segments few-notched, in larger ones ternate below and pinnate upward, with only sparingly lobed pinnules. Margins undulate to shallowly serrate. Exceedingly variable in shape of divisions.

RANGE: Occurring in peninsular Fla. only as intermediates with other taxa; in typical development known from Gadsden Co., Fla., to e. Tex. and northw. [Extending into s. upl. and ne. states to Del. and Ind.]

HABITAT: Moist shaded situations, in pineland, woodland, and swamps, the soil mostly subacid.

CULTURE: Has proved difficult to grow, even in damp woods resembling its native haunts.

NOMENCLATURE:

Botrychium biternatum Underwood, 1896, as to combination, though mistakenly applied to another taxon.
(*Osmunda biternata* Savigny, 1797, basionym; misinterpreted by fern students for over 160 years.)
B. tenuifolium Underwood, 1903, a later epithet for this taxon, mistakenly accepted in many fern books, including *The Fern Guide,* 1961.
B. dissectum var. *tenuifolium* Farwell, invalid.

This taxon intergrades, in Fla., with that treated on the following text-page. Workers who hold that such a situation disfavors species segregation would accordingly combine them, in which case priority requires *biternatum* to become the species epithet and *obliquum* that of subspecies or variety. Here it is deemed simplest to ignore local intergradation, at least until its significance is established. This is consistent with keeping taxa *dissectum* and *obliquum* distinct in the north.

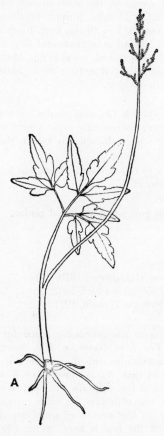

SPARSE-LOBE GRAPE FERN : *Botrychium biternatum*

A. Plant, reduced.

Oblique Grape Fern : *Botrýchium oblìquum*

FEATURES: Plant evergreen, the blade strongly bronzed by cold
even well down in Florida, fruiting in autumn. Stipe *ca.*
2 to 4 and blade-stalk 5 to 10 cm. long. Blade *ca.* 4 to 8 cm.
long and 6 to 12 broad, subternate and then 2- or 3-pinnate
below and pinnately lobed toward tip. Margins shallowly
cut into symmetrical or subserrate teeth. Markedly variable
in details of blade-division.

RANGE: Fla., Highlands Co. and northw., intermediates with
taxon *biternatum;* increasingly typical northw. and westw.
throughout our region. [S. uplands and n. states.]

HABITAT: Chiefly in rather damp woods, but locally in dryish
barrens. Soil subacid.

CULTURE: Can be grown in a woodland garden.

NOMENCLATURE:

Botrychium obliquum Muhlenberg, 1810. (S)
B. dissectum var. *obliquum* Clute, 1902.
B. dissectum f. *obliquum* Fernald, 1921.

The problem as to the acceptable name for this fern was
pointed out in *The Fern Guide,* p. 230. Since in the Great
Lakes region it intergrades with *B. dissectum,* it can be classed
as a subdivision of that. As, however, type *B. dissectum* does
not enter our present region, to use this epithet, without adding
the infra-specific one *obliquum* (in some category), would be
highly confusing. In the interest of simplicity the local intergradation between the two is here (as in *The Fern Guide*)
ignored. *Botrychium dissectum* is treated in the Appendix.

In our region the real difficulty in identifying individual
specimens arises from the intergradation between taxa
obliquum and *biternatum,* and occasional approach of one or
the other of these to taxon *alabamense.* The significance of
these relationships remains to be worked out.

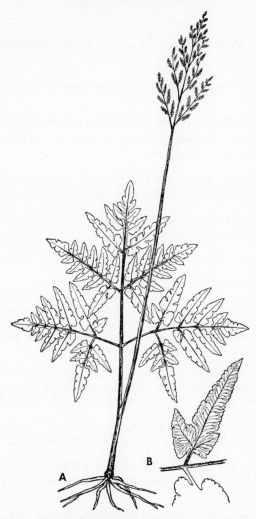

OBLIQUE GRAPE FERN : *Botrychium obliquum*

A. Plant, reduced. B. Pinnule.

7. Water-clover Family : *Marsileàceae*

PILLWORTS : *PILULÀRIA*

Named from Latin for little ball by Linnaeus in 1753.

American Pillwort : *Pilulària americàna* Braun, 1864. (S)

FEATURES: Frond consisting only of a stipe *ca.* 4 to 8 cm. long. Sporocarps globular, tiny.

RANGE: Ga., Washington Co. (lowland) and Walton–Barrow cos. (Piedmont); found here in 1901. [Ark. and Calif.]

HABITAT: Pond shores and temporary pools on granite hills. Soil somewhat acid. Not cultivated.

WATER-CLOVERS : *MARSÍLEA*

Name honoring Marsigli, an Italian naturalist, published by Linnaeus in 1753. Stipe in ours 8 to 15 cm. long, tipped by 2 pairs of triangular pinnae, forming a "4-leaf clover." Sporocarps ovoid. Habitat, sluggish streams and temporary pools. Soil circumneutral. Grown in water-gardens.

Blunt-spine Water-clover : *Marsílea mucronàta* Braun, 1847. (Sometimes, as in (S), confused with *M. vestita*.)

FEATURES: Pinnae *ca.* 6 to 12 mm. long and 5 to 10 broad. Spine-pair above base of sporocarp short and blunt.

RANGE: Fla., Dade and Lake cos.; found here in 1891. Across s. Miss. and La. to Tex. [N. in midlands up to Can.]

Hook-spine Water-clover : *M. uncinàta* Braun, 1847. (S)

FEATURES: Pinnae *ca.* 10 to 20 mm. long and 8 to 15 broad. Spine-pair relatively long, at least the upper hooked.

RANGE: La., Plaquemines Par., up to w. Tenn. and out to Tex.

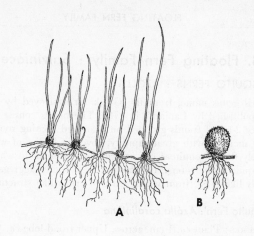

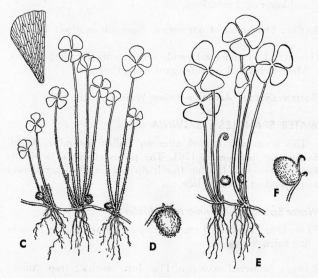

AMERICAN PILLWORT : *Pilularia americana*   A. Plant.

BLUNT-SPINE WATER-CLOVER : *Marsilea mucronata*
C. Plant. **HOOK-SPINE WATER-CLOVER :** *Marsilea un-*
cinata E. Plant. B., D., F., Sporocarps of these, respectively.

8. Floating Fern Family : *Salviniàceae*

MOSQUITO FERNS : *AZÓLLA*

This genus name, from the Greek for destroyed by drying, was published by Lamarck in 1783. The plants consist of tiny bronzy 2-lobed fronds grouped on branched floating rootstocks. They increase with great rapidity, covering bodies of water so densely that mosquitoes can scarcely get through, to which the colloquial name refers. The minute male spores aggregate into a jelly-like mass, from which extrude arrow-like structures.

Mosquito Fern : *Azólla caroliniàna*

FEATURES: Plant *ca.* 1 cm. across. Upper frond-lobe *ca.* ½ mm. and lower *ca.* 2 mm. long.

RANGE: Over most of our region. [Sporadic northw.; W.I.]

HABITAT: Circumneutral ponds and streams; invading ditches. Much cultivated in water gardens and aquaria.

NOMENCLATURE: *Azolla caroliniana* Willdenow, 1810. (S)

WATER SPANGLES : *SALVÍNIA*

This genus was named after an Italian naturalist, A. M. Salvini, by Adanson in 1763. The plants consist of a simple floating rootstock, bearing fronds divided into two aerial oval and a pendent dissected lobe.

Water Spangles : *Salvínia rotundifòlia*

FEATURES: Fronds *ca.* 1 cm. long; upper surface bearing branching hairs.

RANGE: Scattered over pen. Fla. [Intr. northw.; trop. Amer.]

HABITAT and CULTURE: As in *Azolla.*

NOMENCLATURE:

Salvinia rotundifolia Willdenow, 1810.
(Confused with *S. auriculata,* Aublet, 1775, by Small.)

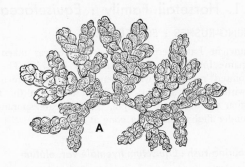

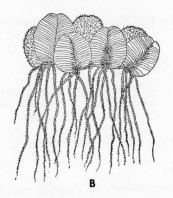

MOSQUITO FERN : *Azolla caroliniana*

A. Plant, enlarged.

WATER-SPANGLES : *Salvinia rotundifolia*

B. Plants.

L 1. Horsetail Family : *Equisetàceae*

SCOURING-RUSHES : *EQUISÈTUM*

An ancient Latin term for horse bristle was taken up as genus name for this group by Linnaeus in 1753. The plants have jointed rootstocks which send up hollow green fluted stems with toothed scarious sheaths at nodes; in the taxa of our region the stems are simple. The delicate sporangia are borne under fleshy scales in a cone at stem-tip.

Tall Scouring-rush : *Equisètum hyemàlè* var. *elàtum*

FEATURES: Stem strongly roughened by silica strips, up to *ca.* 300 cm. high and 2 cm. thick. Sheaths cylindric, lying close against stem. Cone sharp-tipped.

RANGE: Gadsden Co., Fla., up along w. boundary of Ga., and out to Tex.; especially abundant in the Miss. R. flood-plain in La., where forming vast "cane-brakes." [Other vars. over s. uplands, n. N. Amer., and Europe.]

HABITAT: Sandy shores and seemingly barren areas where, however, moisture and nutrients are available at depth; invading disturbed soil, fills, etc. Soil circumneutral.

CULTURE: Too aggressive for garden use.

NOMENCLATURE:

Equisetum hyemale ("*hiemale*") var. *elatum,* Morton, 1951.
(*E. laevigatum γ elatum* Engelmann, 1844, basionym.)
E. prealtum Rafinesque, 1817 [misprint for *praealtum*]. (S)
E. robustum A. Braun, 1844.

Intermediate Scouring-rush : *E.* [×] *ferríssi* Clute, 1904

FEATURES: Differing from the preceding taxon in the stems being only *ca.* ⅛ as large and barely roughened, while the sheaths are flaring.

RANGE: Reported in our region in se. N.C. and w. La.

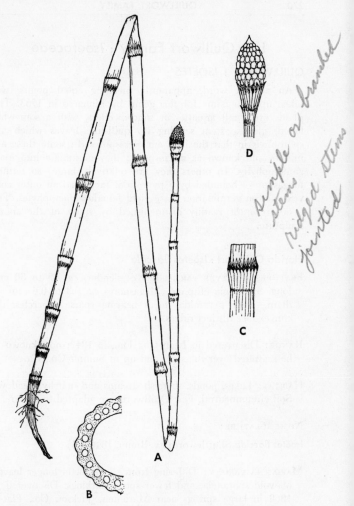

simple or branched stems *ridged stems* *jointed*

TALL SCOURING-RUSH : *Equisetum hyemale* var. *elatum*

A. Plant, reduced.   B. Half-section, enlarged.
C. Node.   D. Cone.

L 2. Quillwort Family : *Isoëtàceae*

QUILLWORTS : *ISÒETES*

An ancient word, apparently meaning equal points, was taken up as a name for this genus by Linnaeus in 1753. The plants are small aquatics or mud-dwellers, with a somewhat lobed, globose stem sending up quill-like leaves which are sporophyls in that the base encloses spores. In some these are minute and known as microspores; they germinate into male gametophytes. In others they are relatively large—so termed megaspores—bounded by 3 pyramidal faces and an outer convex one; on germination these yield female gametophytes. The taxa are most readily distinguished by study of the spore-sculpture.

Florida Quillwort : *Isòëtes fláccida*

FEATURES (of TYPE VAR.): Leaves slender, *ca.* 15 to 30 cm. long. Sporangia ellipsoid. Megaspores *ca.* 0.3 to 0.6 mm. in diam., their pyramidal faces bearing sparse tubercles, the convex face distinct ridges.

RANGE: Discovered in Leon Co., Fla., in 1842; now known to be scattered over the state and up to Sumter Co., Ga.

HABITAT: Lakes, ponds, sluggish streams and marshy meadows. Soil circumneutral. Few Quillworts are adapted to culture.

NOMENCLATURE:

Isoëtes flaccida Shuttleworth *ex*. Braun, 1846. (S)

MARIANNA VARIETY: Differing from the TYPE in longer leaves, obovoid sporangia, and fewer spore-markings. Discovered in 1868 in large springs near Marianna, Jackson Co., Fla. *I. flaccida var. chapmani* Engelmann, 1882. (S)

WINGED VARIETY: Leaves stoutish, winged below. Sporangia spindle-shaped. Spore-markings numerous, crowded. Discovered in 1900 in Sumter Co., Fla., and now known up to s. Ga. *I. flaccida var. alata* Pfeiffer, 1922. (S)

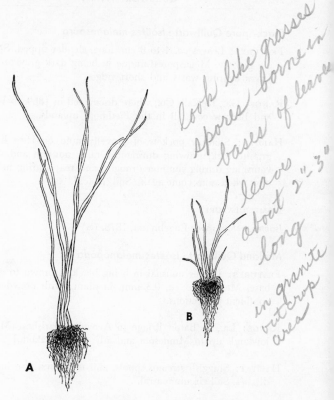

look like grasses
spores borne in
bases of leaves
leaves
about 2"-3"
long
in granite
outcrop
area

FLORIDA QUILLWORT : Isoëtes flaccida
A. Plant.

BLACK-SPORE QUILLWORT : Isoëtes melanospora
B. Plant.

Black-spore Quillwort : *Isòëtes melanospòra*

FEATURES: Leaves *ca.* 4 to 8 cm. long, slender-tipped. Sporangia globose. Megaspores unique in being dark gray to black. Faces bearing warts and short ridges.

RANGE: Ga., DeKalb Co., where discovered in 1869, to Walton and Barrow cos., all in the Piedmont uplands.

HABITAT: Shallow pockets of gravelly mud on bare hills of granite rock; growing during the rainy autumn and winter, vanishing during summer drought, and reappearing in a few days when rains come again. Soil subacid.

NOMENCLATURE:

Isoëtes melanospora Engelmann, 1878. (S)

Midland Quillwort : *Isòëtes melanopòda*

FEATURES: Leaves unusual in being blackish brown to gray at base. Megaspores *ca.* 0.3 mm. in diam., with crowded subconfluent projections.

RANGE: La., E. Baton Rouge to Avoyelles parishes. [Miss. R. lowlands up to Minnesota and adj. South Dakota.]

HABITAT: Sluggish streams, pools, and meadows, also invading ditches. Soil circumneutral.

NOMENCLATURE:

Isoëtes melanopoda Gay & Durieu, 1864. (S)

Appalachian Quillwort : *Isòëtes engelmánni*

FEATURES: Plant relatively coarse. Megaspores averaging 0.5 mm. in diam., the faces honeycomb-reticulate.

RANGE: Fla., Clay–Duval cos., seemingly disjunct; N.C. lowlands, Columbus Co. [S. uplands and n. states.]

NOMENCLATURE:

Isoëtes engelmanni Braun, 1846. (S)

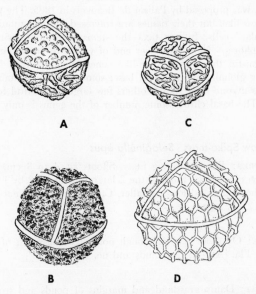

Spores of four QUILLWORTS, enlarged: A. FLORIDA Q. :
Isoëtes flaccida. B. BLACK-SPORE Q. : *I. melanospora.*
C. MIDLAND Q. : *I. melanopoda.* D. APPALACHIAN Q. :
I. engelmanni.

L 3. Spike-moss Family : *Selaginellàceae*

SPIKE-MOSSES : *SELAGINÉLLA*

The name of this genus, a diminutive of the ancient term selago, was proposed by Palisot de Beauvois in 1805. The plants are moss-like, but their tissues are traversed by long tubular or "vascular" cells. In our taxa the stems send down wire-like "rhizophores," from the lower end of which the roots emerge. At stem-tip there arise spike-like cones of sporophyls—leaves bearing globular sporangia at base; some of these contain numerous minute male spores, others few large tetrahedral female ones. The basal chromosome number of the genus is only 9.

Meadow Spike-moss : *Selaginélla àpus*

FEATURES: Plants forming mats. Shoots *ca.* 4 to 8 cm. high. Leaves in 4 rows, those of the 2 lateral up to *ca.* 2 by 1 mm., of the upper and lower smaller. Cone rounded-prismatic, *ca.* 1 to 2 cm. long.

RANGE: Over our region, though not extending south of Polk Co., Fla. [Also in s. uplands and ne. states.]

HABITAT: Damp grassland and margins of ponds and streams, sometimes invading disturbed ground. Soil circumneutral to subacid. Not cultivated.

NOMENCLATURE:

Selagineila apus Spring, 1840; *apoda* Fernald, 1915.
(*Lycopodium apodum* L., 1753, basionym.)
Diplostachyum apodum Palisot de Beauvois, 1805. (S)

In Latin as used in 1840 the appropriate form of this epithet was *apus,* as pointed out by Spring; according to Fernald, however, it should be *apoda,* and he is followed by some current workers.

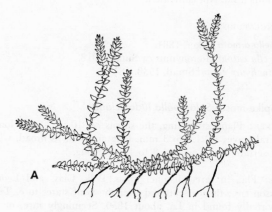

MEADOW SPIKE-MOSS : *Selaginella apus*

A. Plant.

Armored Spike-moss : *Selaginélla armàta*

FEATURES: Plants forming small mats, the shoots *ca.* 1.5 to 3 cm. long. Lateral leaves *ca.* 1 mm. long, close-set, thickish-margined, resembling the plates on a midget suit of armor. Cone rounded-prismatic, *ca.* 2 to 4 cm. long.

RANGE: Fla., Dade–Monroe cos., where found in 1903. [Cuba.]

HABITAT: Mossy limestone ledges and small sink margins. Soil circumneutral. Not cultivated.

NOMENCLATURE:

Selaginella armata Baker, 1884.
Selaginella eatoni Hieronymus *ex* Small, 1918.
Diplostachyum eatoni Small, 1938. (S)

Gulf Spike-moss : *Selaginélla ludoviciàna*

FEATURES: Plants straggling, the shoots *ca.* 10 to 20 cm. long. Lateral leaves *ca.* 1.5 to 3 mm. long and half as broad, with firm serrate rim. Cone *ca.* 8 to 15 cm. long.

RANGE: Fla., in three disjunct areas, Polk, Clay, and Leon–Jackson cos.; thence scattered over the Gulf states to e. Tex. Reportedly found in La. about 1850. Seemingly rare, or at least little-collected.

HABITAT: Swamp margins, moist grassy openings in pineland, sometimes invading disturbed ground. Soil circumneutral.

CULTURE: Said to have been cultivated in Europe from *ca.* 1850 on, but seemingly not in the United States.

NOMENCLATURE:

Selaginella ludoviciana Braun, 1860.
Diplostachyum ludovicianum Small, 1938. (S)

Several Asian Spike-mosses have been observed as escapes in our region; their features are briefly described on the following text-page.

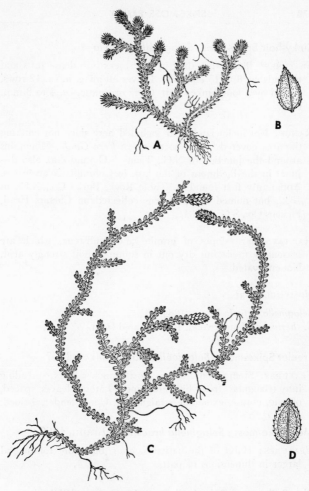

ARMORED SPIKE-MOSS : *Selaginella armata*

A. Plant.   B. Leaf, enlarged.

GULF SPIKE-MOSS : *S. ludoviciana*

C. Plant.   D. Leaf, enlarged.

Kinky-hair Spike-moss : *Selaginélla tortípila*

FEATURES: Plants spreading by rootstocks into dense tufts and mounds *ca.* 8 to 15 cm. high. Leaves all alike, in *ca.* 12 rows, tipped by a long kinked hair. Cone prismatic, *ca.* 4 to 8 mm. long.

RANGE: Not in lowlands, but included here since not entering the area covered by the northeastern *Fern Guide*. Mountains around the junction of N.C., Tenn., S.C., and Ga., also disjunct in the Piedmont of the last, in Columbia–Warren cos. Apparently first found on Table Rock, Burke Co., N.C., in 1839, but named on specimens collected on Caesars Head, Pickens Co., S.C., in 1841.

HABITAT: Bare slopes of granite and sandstone, which are seasonally moist but dry out in summer. Soil strongly acid. Not cultivated.

NOMENCLATURE:

Selaginella tortipila Braun, 1865. (S)
S. sherwoodii Underwood, 1902, stunted form.

Treelet Spike-moss : *Selaginélla braùnii* Baker, 1867.

FEATURES: Stem woody, straw-color; branches hairy, spreading into triangular frond-like groupings. Lateral leaves spaced, oblong, obtuse, extending straight out. Cone slender, 4-sided.

Mat Spike-moss : *Selaginélla kraùssiana* Braun, 1860.

FEATURES: Habit of the native *S. apus,* but more robust and larger in dimensions of parts.

Blue Spike-moss: *Selaginélla uncinàta* Spring, 1850.

FEATURES: Intermediate in aspect between the above two taxa. Leaves bright blue-green. Cone *ca.* 15 mm. long.

Vine Spike-moss : *Selaginélla willdenòvii* Baker, 1867.

FEATURES: Stem climbing, with fan-like gray-green branchlet groups *ca.* 15 cm. across. Cone *ca.* 2.5 cm. long.

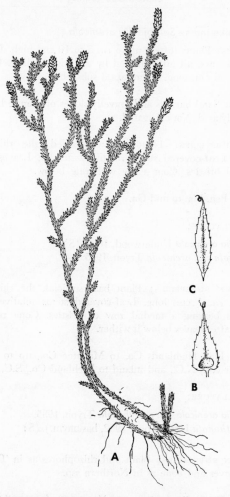

KINKY-HAIR SPIKE-MOSS : *Selaginella tortipila*

A. Plant.   Leaves with hair-tip, enlarged:
B. Fertile.   C. Sterile.

Sand Spike-moss : *Selaginélla arenícola*

FEATURES: Plants tufted, up to *ca.* 5 to 10 cm. high. Leaves in *ca.* 8 rows, all alike, tipped by a straight bristle. Cone *ca.* 10 to 20 cm. long. There are 3 subspecies.

HABITAT: Sand barrens and gravelly slopes of granite hills. Soil strongly acid. Not cultivated.

TYPE SUBSPECIES: Plant-base well-buried, the rhizophores short. Leaf-covered stems relatively slender. Leaves lacking medial bristles. Cone early withering below.

RANGE: Pen. Fla. to mid-Ga.

NOMENCLATURE:

Selaginella arenicola Underwood, 1898. (S)
S. arenicola ssp. *arenicola* Tryon, 1955.

NORTHERN SUBSPECIES: Plant base surficial, the rhizophores aerial, *ca.* 1 cm. long. Leaf-covered stems relatively stout. Leaves bearing a medial row of bristles. Cone remaining green after leaves below it wither.

RANGE: Fla., Highlands Co. to Manatee Co., up to Bladen–Pender cos., N.C., and inland to Richland Co., S.C.

NOMENCLATURE:

Selaginella arenicola ssp. *acanthonota* Tryon, 1955.
(*S. acanthonota* Underwood, 1902, basionym.) (S)

WESTERN SUBSPECIES: Plant and rhizophores as in Type ssp., but leaves and cone as in Northern ssp.

RANGE: Gradational forms, w. Ala. to ne. La.; well differentiated ones, w. La. to mid-Tex.

NOMENCLATURE:

Selaginella arenicola ssp. *riddellii* Tryon, 1955.
(*S. riddellii* Van Eseltine, 1918, basionym.)

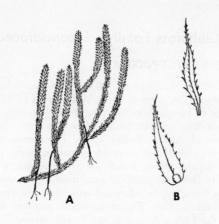

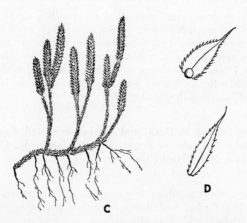

SAND SPIKE-MOSS : *Selaginella arenicola*. NORTHERN :
ssp. *acanthonota*. A. Plant. B. Leaves, enlarged. TYPE
SUBSPECIES. C. Plant. D. Leaves, enlarged.

L 4. Clubmoss Family : *Lycopodiàceae*

CLUBMOSSES : *LYCOPÒDIUM*

The ancient Greek name for these plants, signifying wolf's foot, was adopted as a genus name by Linnaeus in 1753. The plants consist of rootstocks or creeping stems with rather coarse roots. The erect or arching stems and branches are clothed by multiple rows of small scale-like leaves. The spores, all alike, are formed in globular to ellipsoid sporangia, borne near the base of specialized leaves, which are correspondingly termed sporophyls. In the most primitive taxa these are in zones along the stems or branches; in advanced ones, they are grouped in terminal cylindric cones. The chromosome numbers vary, but are among the highest known in the Pteridophytes.

Nodding Clubmoss : *Lycopòdium cernùum*

FEATURES: Stem erect, ascending, or vine-like, up to *ca*. 50 cm. long, much branched, rooting at intervals when contacting moist humus, densely leafy and resembling a tiny coniferous tree. Leaves narrow-triangular, somewhat curved, *ca*. 2 to 4 mm. long. Cones numerous, sessile and nodding at branchlet tip, *ca*. 5 to 10 mm. long. Sporangia tiny, borne on broad coarse-toothed sporophyls.

RANGE: Fla. up to Duval and Alachua cos., and disjunct in Gadsden Co.; also to Brantly and Randolph cos., Ga., and out to s. Miss. [World tropics.]

HABITAT: Moist meadows, bog margins, and stream banks, also invading ditches and damp cuts, then becoming vine-like. Soil strongly acid. Not cultivated.

NOMENCLATURE:

Lycopodium cernuum L., 1753. (S)
Lepidotis cernua Palisot de Beauvois, 1805.

NODDING CLUBMOSS : *Lycopodium cernuum*

A. Plant, reduced.   B. Fertile leaf, enlarged.

Slender Clubmoss : *Lycopòdium caroliniànum*

FEATURES: Stem moderately long, prostrate, the broadish falcate lateral leaves conspicuous. Erect fertile branches few,
ca. 13 to 25 cm. tall, with scattered scale-like leaves. Cone
slender, pale, *ca.* 4 to 8 cm. long.

RANGE: Scattered throughout Fla., up to e. N.C., and out to
e. Tex. [Sparingly n. near coast to L.I., N.Y. Identical or
related taxa occur over world subtropics.]

HABITAT: Sphagnous meadows and wet sandy flats. Soil strongly
acid. Not cultivated.

NOMENCLATURE:

Lycopodium carolinianum L., 1753. (S)

Tight-leaf Clubmoss : *Lycopòdium appréssum*

FEATURES: Stem elongate, prostrate and rooting throughout,
with numerous narrow leaves. Erect fertile branches several,
ca. 15 to 30 cm. tall, with copious appressed leaves. Cone
slender as a result of the sporophyls being closely appressed,
ca. 2.5 to 5 cm. long.

RANGE: Fla., Highlands and Hillsborough cos., up to N.C. and
out to e. Tex. [N. lowlands and rarely uplands.]

HABITAT: Bogs, sphagnous meadows, and wet sand barrens.
Soil strongly acid. Not cultivated.

NOMENCLATURE:

Lycopodium appressum [original spelling of epithet] (S); *L.
adpressum* Lloyd & Underwood, 1900, invalid change.
(*L. inundatum* v. *appressum* Chapman, 1878, basionym.)
L. inundatum β bigelovii Tuckerman, 1843, in part.

This taxon at times seems to grade into others growing
nearby, but as this may well be due to hybridization, it is here
treated as an independent species.

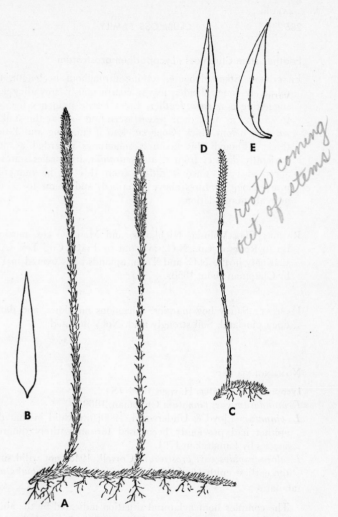

roots coming out of stems

TIGHT-LEAF CLUBMOSS : *Lycopodium appressum*

A. Plant, reduced.   B. Stem-leaf, enlarged.

SLENDER CLUBMOSS : *L. carolinianum*

C. Plant, reduced.   D. Top and   E. Side stem-leaf.

Feather-stem Clubmoss : *Lycopòdium prostràtum*

FEATURES: Stem elongate, rooting throughout its length, the relatively long, slender leaves conspicuously spreading and suggesting a narrow feather. Erect fertile branches few, up to *ca.* 35 cm. tall, their leaves ascending so that the stalk is *ca.* 4 to 8 mm. thick. Cone *ca.* 4 to 8 cm. long and 1 to 2 thick. Although this taxon is sometimes regarded as only varietally distinct from *t. alopecuroides,* its species status is accepted here, since it differs from this in the numerous morphologic features above described, and seems to exhibit no real intergradation.

RANGE: Fla., Volusia, Highlands, and Manatee cos. northw., up to Robeson Co., N.C., and out to Travis Co., Tex. [Also sparingly in the N.C. and Tenn. uplands.] Discovered in Fla. by Chapman about 1850.

HABITAT: Sandy bog margins, sphagnous meadows, and damp open pineland. Soil strongly acid. Not cultivated.

NOMENCLATURE:

Lycopodium prostratum Harper, 1906. (S)
L. inundatum var. *pinnatum* Chapman, 1860.
L. pinnatum Lloyd & Underwood, 1900; not valid in that this epithet had previously been used for an entirely different species by Lamarck in 1791.
L. alopecuroides var. *prostratum* Correll, 1948; not valid since the earliest epithet published in varietal status was *pinnatum.*

The complex nomenclatorial situation indicated by the above tabulation illustrates how careful one must be to follow the dictates of the rule of priority. The eminent pioneer A. W. Chapman classed this taxon as a variety, then Lloyd & Underwood raised it to species rank, overlooking that the epithet had been used over 100 years before. Recognizing this, Harper published a new epithet, which Correll proceeded to reduce to varietal rank, although in that rank Chapman's had priority.

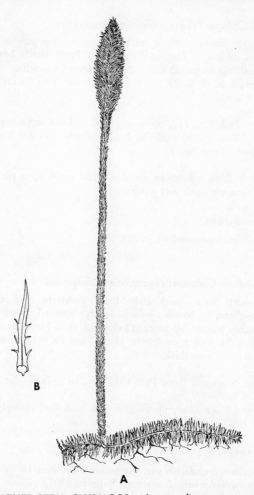

FEATHER-STEM CLUBMOSS : *Lycopodium prostratum*

A. Plant, reduced.   B. Fertile leaf, enlarged.

Foxtail Clubmoss : *Lycopòdium alopecuroìdes*

FEATURES: Stem elongate, arching, and rooting only at ends, its leaves not in feather-like pattern. Erect fertile branches several, up to *ca.* 35 cm. tall, their leaves spreading so that the stalk is 10 to 20 cm. thick. Cone *ca.* 5 to 10 cm. long and 2 thick.

RANGE: Polk Co., Fla., up to ne. N.C. and out to Orange Co., Tex. [Also sparingly in the N.C. uplands, and ne. lowlands to Conn. Trop. Amer.]

HABITAT: Bogs, sphagnous meadows, and moist open pineland. Soil strongly acid. Not cultivated.

NOMENCLATURE:

Lycopodium alopecuroides L., 1753. (S)

Intermediate Clubmoss : *Lycopòdium chapmáni*

FEATURES: Stem moderately long, prostrate and rooting throughout, its leaves tending to curve upward. Erect fertile branches several, up to *ca.* 25 cm. tall, their leaves ascending so that the stalk is *ca.* 5 mm. thick. Cone *ca.* 3 to 6 cm. long and 6 to 12 mm. thick.

RANGE: Scattered from Polk Co., Fla., to e. N.C. [Ne. lowl.]

HABITAT: Moist sandy openings in pineland. Soil strongly acid. Not cultivated.

NOMENCLATURE:

Lycopodium inundatum var. *elongatum* Chapman, 1878.
L. alopecuroides var. *elongatum* Chapman, 1897.
L. chapmani Underwood *ex* Maxon, 1901, restricted.

This taxon is little known, and may prove to be a hybrid. The accepted epithet was applied by Underwood to two taxa; as the first had been assigned the species epithet *appressum* the year before, it is the second which needs one.

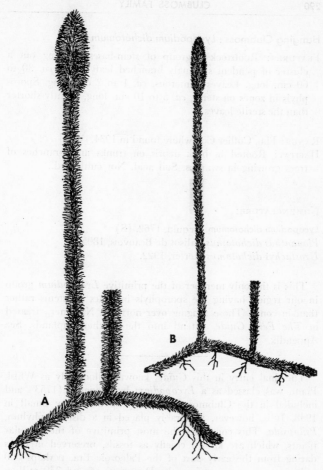

FOXTAIL CLUBMOSS : *Lycopodium alopecuroides*

A. Plant, reduced.

INTERMEDIATE CLUBMOSS : *L. chapmani*

B. Plant, reduced.

289

Hanging Clubmoss : *Lycopòdium dichótomum*

FEATURES: Rootstock a group of stem-bases, sending out a cluster of pendent sparingly branched leafy stems *ca.* 30 to 60 cm. long. Leaves numerous, *ca.* 1 to 2 cm. long. Sporophyls in zones on stems, *ca.* 5 to 10 cm. long, slightly shorter than the sterile leaves.

RANGE: Fla., Collier Co., where found in 1934. [W.I.]

HABITAT: Rooted in bark debris on trunks and branches of trees growing in swamps. Soil acid. Not cultivated.

NOMENCLATURE:

Lycopodium dichotomum Jacquin, 1762. (S)
Plananthus dichotomus Palisot de Beauvois, 1805.
Urostachys dichotomus Herter, 1922.

This is the only member of the primitive *Lycopodium* group in our region having the sporophyls in zones on stems rather than in cones. Those ranging over northern N. Amer., treated in *The Fern Guide,* extend into the southern uplands. See Appendix.

———————

The final entry in this *Guide,* known colloquially as Whisk Plant, was classed as a *Lycopodium* by Linnaeus (1753) and included in the Clubmoss Order, *Lycopodiales,* by Small in 1938. It is, however, preferably placed in a distinct phylum, *Psilopsida.* This comprises the most primitive of the vascular plants, which are known chiefly as fossils, preserved in rocks dating from the early part of the Paleozoic Era, perhaps 500 million years ago, and into the Devonian, around 350 million years ago. Although from that time on fossil records are sporadic, members of the phylum survived somewhere on earth, and evolved into a few extant ones in the world tropics. These are characterized by the absence of roots but the presence of a rootstock continuous with the stem, both traversed by a simplified vascular system. Instead of leaves they bear only scales, photosynthesis being carried on by the green stem. Our one taxon is notable in having scattered 3-lobed sporangia.

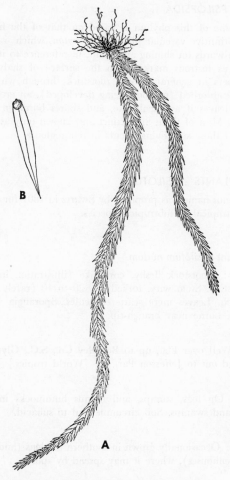

HANGING CLUBMOSS : *Lycopodium dichotomum*

A. Plant. B. Fertile leaf, enlarged.

PHYLUM *PSILÓPSIDA*

The name of this phylum is based on that of the first discovered primitive vascular plant, *Psilophyton,* which was from the Greek words for shining and plant, in reference to its being fossilized as lustrous markings on the surface of shaly rocks. Its members in general have a rootstock through which nutrients are absorbed (no roots being developed), an erect stem with the leaves if any scale-like, and spores borne in simple sporangia. Most of them are extinct and known only as fossils, but one of those still living occurs in our region.

WHISK PLANTS : *PSILÒTUM*

This genus name was proposed by Swartz in 1801 for a small group of tropical or subtropical species.

Whisk Plant : *Psilòtum nùdum*

FEATURES: Rootstock fleshy, coral-like (illustration in Small unrealistic). Stem wiry, forked, *ca.* 20 to 40 (rarely to 75) cm. high. Leaves mere scattered scales. Sporangia solitary, 3-lobed, borne near branch-tip.

RANGE: Well over Fla., up to Berkeley Co., S.C., Glynn Co., Ga., and out to Jefferson Par., La. [World tropics.]

HABITAT: On logs, stumps, and humus hummocks in damp woods and swamps. Soil circumneutral to subacid.

CULTURE: Occasionally grown in southern gardens (and northern greenhouses), where it may spread by spores.

NOMENCLATURE:

Psilotum nudum Grisebach, 1857. (S)
(*Lycopodium nudum* L., 1753, basionym.)
Psilotum triquetrum Swartz, 1801, invalid later epithet.

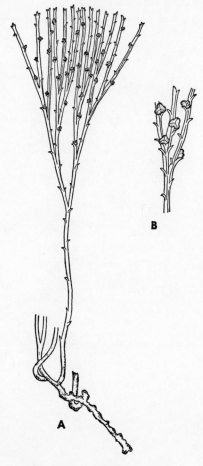

WHISK PLANT : *Psilotum nudum*

A. Plant, reduced.   B. Branchlets, with sporangia.

APPENDIX

Ferns of the Southern Uplands

The ferns discussed thus far comprise those which grow (1) only in the southern lowlands, (2) in localized areas at moderate elevations in the southern uplands but not farther north, and (3) in both of these regions as well as up over northeastern North America. Not covered are a number which are chiefly northern, but which range across the conventional boundary line at north latitude 36° 30′ above a few hundred feet altitude, barely if at all descending into the lowlands. As naturalists in the uplands may need help in identifying these, yet not have a copy of *The Fern Guide* at hand, the plates from that work representing the 30 of them which occur with such frequency that they are fairly certain to be encountered are here republished in reduced format, with pertinent descriptive data. Taxa so rare that they are likely to be located only by specialists are briefly discussed, though not illustrated.

Genera and species are taken up in a sequence corresponding to that previously followed, but the data given under successive headings are based on observations actually made in the southern upland region. Small's *Ferns of the Southeastern States* covers taxa known in the uplands at that time, and the names adopted therein are indicated by (S). Correspondingly, those favored in *The Fern Guide* are designated by (FG). Names used only in this Appendix are not included in the indexes to the present *Guide*.

Rock-cap Fern : *Polypodium virginianum*

FEATURES: Rootstock-scales shining brown, with hairlike tip. Fronds glabrous throughout. Stipe *ca.* ⅔ as long as blade, which in type form is *ca.* 10 to 20 cm. long and 3 to 6 broad, in a small one resp. 5 to 10 and 2 to 4. Segments obtusish to acutish. Sori 1 to 2 mm. across, yellow, aging brown. In the cut are also 3 others which occur in southern uplands.

RANGE: Piedmont N.C. to w. Ark., increasingly rare southward to Clarke Co., Ga., and far n. Ala.

HABITAT: Partly shaded dry rocky slopes, often, as indicated by the colloquial name, capping rock ledges. Soil mostly subacid.

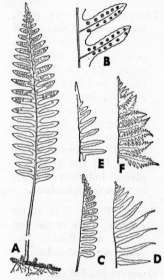

ROCK-CAP FERN
A. Plant, reduced. B. Segments, large phase. Half blades of forms:
C. Small. D. Tapering.
E. Broad-based. F. Frilled.

CULTURE: Can be transplanted to humus hummocks and, if kept moist until it takes hold, to shaded rocks.

NOMENCLATURE:

Polypodium virginianum L., 1753. (S, FG)
P. vulgare var. *virginianum* A. Eaton, 1818.

Cliff Ferns (*Woodsia*): In addition to the representative of this genus treated on p. 80, two others have been found here rarely on northwest-facing rock ledges:
Rusty Cliff Fern, *Woodsia ilvensis* R. Brown, 1813 (S, FG), at one station in Ashe Co., N.C.
Appalachian Cliff Fern, *Woodsia appalachiana* Taylor, 1947 (FG), at one station each in Polk Co., N.C., Johnson and Unicoi cos., Tenn., and Logan Co., Ark.

Bulblet Fern : *Cystopteris bulbifera*

FEATURES: Rootstock short, brown-scaly, holding old stipe-bases. Stipe short, pinkish. Blade long-triangular, often *ca.* 23 to 45 cm. lg. and 8 to 15 broad at base, lax, the pinnae cut into toothed pinnules and segments. Rachis and pinna-axes beneath bearing several globose bulblets which fall and yield new plants. Indusium truncate at tip, sparse-glandular.

RANGE: Far w. N.C. to far e. Okla., down to nw. cor. of Ga. and Etowah Co., Ala. Locally abundant.

HABITAT: Shaded outcrops of limestone and other calcareous rocks. Soil circumneutral.

BULBLET FERN
A. Plant, reduced.   B. Pinnule and
C. Sorus, enlarged.

CULTURE: Spreads rapidly in a shady rock garden.

NOMENCLATURE:

Cystopteris bulbifera Bernhardi, 1806. (S, FG)
(*Polypodium bulbiferum* L., 1753, basionym.)

On shaded rocks from far w. N.C. to Ark. and down to ne. Ala. also occurs: Upland Brittle Fern, *Cystopteris fragilis* v. *mackayi* Lawson, 1829. This differs from the Lowland Brittle Fern (p. 82) in having a short scaly rootstock and smaller fronds. There are also hybrids.

Northern Beech Fern, *Phegopteris connectilis* Watt, 1866 (FG), differing from the Southern (p. 84) in its narrower basal pinna-pair and more copious scales, is known at two especially cool stations in the N.C. mountains.

Tapering Fern : *Thelypteris noveboracensis*

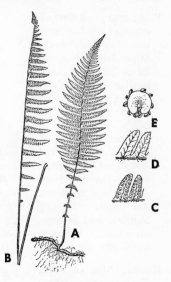

FEATURES: Fronds yellowish green, short-stiped, the fertile taller and narrower than sterile. Blade *ca.* 25 to 50 cm. long and 8 to 15 broad, tapering gradually downward, the lowest pinnae being mere wings. Pinnae cut into bluntish oblong entire segments. Rachis, midribs, and simple veins hairy beneath.

RANGE: Fairly common, N.C. and Tenn. down to Ga. and Ala.; also at one station in Hot Springs Co., Ark. Rarely descending across the Fall Line into lowlands.

HABITAT: Woods, thickets, and swamps, in moderately acid humus-rich soil.

TAPERING FERN
A. *Plant with sterile frond, reduced.*
B. *Half fertile frond, reduced.*
C. *Fertile and* D. *Sterile segments.*
E. *Sorus, enlarged.*

CULTURE: Readily grown in a woodland garden, the odd blade-shape producing an interesting effect. Spreads by rootstocks, but rarely unduly rapidly.

NOMENCLATURE:

Thelypteris noveboracensis Nieuwland, 1910. (S, FG)
(*Polypodium noveboracense* L., 1753, basionym.)
Aspidium noveboracense Swartz, 1801.
Lastrea noveboracensis Presl, 1836.
Dryopteris noveboracensis Gray, 1848.

This taxon is considered to belong to the Marsh Fern Group, or *Thelypteris* proper, represented herein (p. 102) by *T. palustris,* although it diverges in chromosome number to an unusual extent, counts of 27 and 29 having been reported on it, as compared with 35.

Silvery Glade Fern : *Athyrium thelypterioides*

FEATURES: Rootstock creeping, sending up a row of thickish fronds. Stipe dark below, *ca.* 20 to 40 cm. long, bearing copious fragile n a r r o w scales. Blade fine-scaly beneath, *ca.* 35 to 70 cm. long and 13 to 25 b r o a d, narrowed downward. Pinnae deeply cut into truncate oblong segments, the inner forming auricles. Sori in regular rows; indusium transiently silvery.

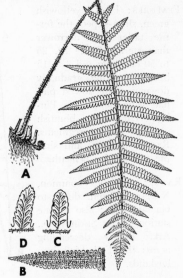

RANGE: Mts. of N.C., Tenn., and n. Ala., and rarely in Piedmont and lowlands, as noted on p. 128.

SILVERY GLADE FERN
A. Plant, reduced.   **B.** *Pinna.*
Segments of: **C.** *Type form and*
D. *Toothed form.*

HABITAT: Damp woods and cool shaded slopes, the soil rich in humus and usually subacid.

CULTURE: Readily grown in a woodland garden, but spready.

NOMENCLATURE:

Athyrium thelypterioides Desvaux, 1827. (S, FG)
(*Asplenium thelypterioides* Michaux, 1803, basionym.)
Diplazium thelypterioides Presl, 1806.
Diplazium acrostichoides Butters, 1917.
(*Asplenium acrostichoides* Swartz, 1801, basionym.)

———————

A striking relative of a lowland taxon (p. 126) with blade up to *ca.* 60 cm. long and 40 broad, high in the mts. of N.C. and Tenn., is tentatively named the **Lacy Southern Lady Fern,** *Athyrium asplenioides* f. *subtripinnatum* Butters, 1917 (FG).

Narrow Swamp Fern : *Dryopteris cristata*

FEATURES: Rootstock bearing brd. pale-brown scales. Stipe *ca.* 13 to 25 cm. lg., sparsely scaly. Blade dimorphic, the evergreen sterile ones *ca.* 15 to 30 cm. long, 6 to 12 broad, the tardily deciduous fertile resp. 25 to 50 and 8 to 15. Pinnae tending to turn crosswise to blade, the lower triangular and upper oblong, deeply cut into toothed segments. Sori medial. Indusium large, glabrous.

RANGE: Rare and scattered, N.C. Piedmont and mts. to far ne. Tenn.

HABITAT: Swamps, wet thickets, and springy slopes, the soil mostly subacid.

NARROW SWAMP FERN
A. *Plant, reduced.* B. *Sterile and*
C. *Fertile pinna.*

CULTURE: Desirable for a moist garden, the narrow blades with turned pinnae yielding a striking effect.

NOMENCLATURE:

Dryopteris cristata Gray, 1848. (S, FG)
(*Polypodium cristatum* L., 1753, basionym.)
Aspidium cristatum Swartz, 1801.
Nephrodium cristatum Michaux, 1803.

Reports of the occurrence of this species in the Miss. River lowlands of La. and Ark. were noted on p. 144. At least those from the former state are based on fragmentary specimens collected many years ago, and this fern has apparently never been rediscovered here in recent times.

Giant Wood Fern : *Dryopteris goldiana*

FEATURES: Rootstock-scales shining blackish brown. Stipe *ca.* 25 to 50 cm. lg., its scales medially brown-striped. Blade of varying green hues, *ca.* 30 to 60 cm. long and 20 to 40 brd., tardily deciduous, o v a t e, abruptly contracted toward tip. Pinnae cut into subfalcate segments, varying in length and yielding an undulate lower pinna-outline. S o r i near midvein. Indusia glabrous.

RANGE: Mts. of N.C. to Franklin Co., Tenn., down to far n. S.C., Ga., and Ala.

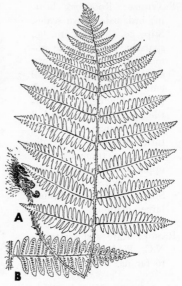

GIANT WOOD FERN
A. *Plant, reduced.* B. *Fertile pinna.*

HABITAT: Wooded rocky slopes, flats, and stream banks, the soil usually circumneutral.

CULTURE: Desirable in a woodland garden.

NOMENCLATURE:

Dryopteris goldiana Gray, 1848. (S, FG)
(*Aspidium goldianum* Hooker, 1822, basionym.)
Nephrodium goldianum Hooker & Greville, 1829.

The **Broad Swamp Fern**, *Dryopteris clintoniana* Dowell, 1906 (S, FG), is sometimes confused with the above Wood Fern, but differs in the scales being paler brown, the uniformly green blade only *ca.* 13 to 35 cm. broad and gradually tapering upward, and the pinna-outline not undulate. It has been reported from one Piedmont station in Mecklenburg Co., N.C.

Marginal Wood Fern : *Dryopteris marginalis*

FEATURES: Rootstock tipped with copious yellow-brown scales which extend well up the *ca.* 15- to 30-cm.-long stipe. Blade grayish green, leathery, evergreen, *ca.* 25 to 50 cm. long and 13 to 25 broad. Pinnae deeply cut into obtuse round-lobed or shallowly toothed segments. Sori lying close to but not touching margins, or some near segment-base. Indusium glabrous.

RANGE: Piedmont N.C. to e. Okla., down to De Kalb Co., Ga., and n. Ala.; barely crossing the Fall Line.

HABITAT: Rocky or rarely clayey slopes, sunny or shady; soil low in nutrients and subacid to circumneutral.

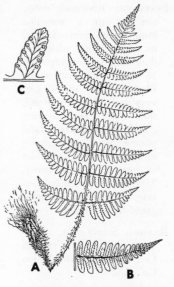

MARGINAL WOOD FERN
A. *Plant, reduced.*   B. *Pinna.*
C. *Fertile segment.*

CULTURE: Easily grown in almost any well-drained situation, and desirable by virtue of its being fully evergreen, and its ability to lessen erosion on slopes.

NOMENCLATURE:

Dryopteris marginalis Gray, 1848. (S, FG)
(*Polypodium marginale* L., 1753, basionym.)
Aspidium marginale Swartz, 1801.
Nephrodium marginale Michaux, 1803.

This species seems able to cross with most other members of the genus, the hybrids combining the features of the parents in a striking way. The presence of copious long stipe-scales characterizes such crosses.

Fancy Fern : *Dryopteris intermedia*

FEATURES: Rootstock erect, sending up a vase-like group of evergreen fronds, its scales broad with medial dark stripe. Stipe *ca.* 13 to 25 cm. long, scaly. Blade *ca.* 25 to 50 cm. long and 13 to 25 broad, the upper axes bearing gland-tipped hairs. Basal pinnae often with innermost b o t t o m pinnules shorter than next outer. Margins divergently serrate. Indusium bearing gland-tipped hairs.

RANGE: Stanly Co., Piedmont N.C., to Franklin Co., s. Tenn., and Union Co., Ga.

HABITAT: Wooded rocky slopes and hummocks in swamps, the soil rich in humus and subacid to circumneutral.

FANCY FERN
A. Plant, reduced. B. Pinnule.
C. Sorus, enlarged.

CULTURE: A most desirable fern for the woodland garden.

NOMENCLATURE:

Dryopteris intermedia Gray, 1848. (S, FG)
(*Polypodium intermedium* Muhlenberg, 1810, a synonym of *Aspidium intermedium* Willdenow, 1810, basionyms.)
D. spinulosa var. *intermedia* Underwood, 1893.
D. austriaca var. *intermedia* Morton, 1950.

The **Toothed Wood Fern,** *Dryopteris spinulosa* Watt, 1867, differs from the above in having fewer evergreen fronds in a row, paler scales, no glands whatever, innermost bottom pinnules always longest, and teeth sub-appressed. It has been reported at one station each in upland N.C., S.C., Tenn., and Ark.

Mountain Wood Fern : *Dryopteris dilatata*, relative

FEATURES: Fronds close-set, early deciduous. Stipe *ca.* 18 to 35 cm. long, with medially dark scales. Blade *ca.* 30 to 60 cm. lg. and 20 to 40 broad, 2-pinnate with the pinnules cut into sharply s e r r a t e segments, yielding a lacy pattern. Innermost bottom pinnule about as long as next outer, so broad as to match width of 2 short upper ones. Sori r a t h e r small, medial; indusium glabrous or occasionally bearing glands.

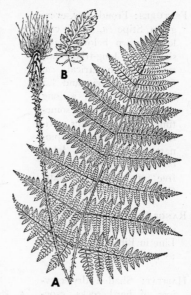

MOUNTAIN WOOD FERN
A. *Plant, reduced.* B. *Pinnule.*

RANGE: In the higher mts. of N.C., S.C., and Tenn.

HABITAT: Wooded rocky slopes and swamp-margins, in cool humus-rich mostly subacid soil.

CULTURE: Highly ornamental and worth growing in a woodland garden where the soil remains cool in summer.

NOMENCLATURE: Some workers hold this fern to be identical with *Polypodium austriacum* Jacquin, 1765, of the Alps, but the detailed description of that does not correspond.

Dryopteris dilatata Gray, 1848, relative. (FG)
(*Polypodium dilatatum* Hoffmann, 1848, basionym.)
D. spinulosa v. *americana* Fernald, 1915, invalid.
(*Aspidium s.* v. *a.* Fischer, 1848, basionym, provisional.)
D. campyloptera Clarkson, 1930, invalid. (S)
(*Aspidium c.* Kunze, 1848, basionym, provisional.)

Lobed Spleenwort : *Asplenium pinnatifidum*

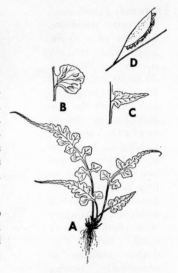

FEATURES: Fronds few, ever-green. Stipe *ca.* 4 to 8 cm. long, brown below. Blade simple, long-triangular, rather unsymmetrical, *ca.* 6 to 12 cm. long and 1.5 to 3 broad, with a long slender tip which some-times roots. Margins vari-ably lobed, often subpin-nate below, the lobes obtuse to acuminate. Veins free or a few areolate. Cytologically tetraploid.

RANGE: Piedmont N.C. to e. Okla., down to the Fall Line in Bibb Co., Ga., and to n.-centr. Ala.

HABITAT: Shaded dry crev-ices of hard rocks, espe-cially sandstone and gneiss. Soil low in nutrients and acid or rarely circumneu-tral.

LOBED SPLEENWORT
A. *Plant. Segments of:* B. *Blunt and* C. *Tapering variants.*
D. *Sorus, enlarged.*

CULTURE: Scarcely possible, since the sort of habitat required can not be constructed artificially.

NOMENCLATURE:

Asplenium pinnatifidum Nuttall, 1818. (S, FG)
(*A. rhizophyllum β pinnatifidum* Muhlenberg, 1813, basionym.)

Cytologic study indicates that this tetraploid species orig-inated as a hybrid between the Mountain Spleenwort and the Walking Fern (discussed later), in which the chromosomes subsequently doubled. This accounts for the way in which it combines the characters of these parents, as well as its marked variability, even in respect to the soil conditions it favors.

Mountain Spleenwort : *Asplenium montanum*

FEATURES: Moderately variable in response to differences in availability of moisture, nutrients, etc. Fronds numerous, evergreen. Stipe *ca.* 3.5 to 7 mm. long, brown at base. Blade of general oblong outline, *ca.* 4 to 8 cm. long and 2 to 4 broad, 1- to 3-pinnate. Pinnae and pinnules subopposite, elliptic to rhombic, varying from merely serrate to cut into slender segments. Sori few, medial.

RANGE: Piedmont N.C. to c. Tenn., down to Lincoln Co., Ga., and Bibb Co., Ala.

HABITAT: Shaded damp crevices in sandstone, gneiss, and other hard non-calcareous rocks. Soil strongly acid.

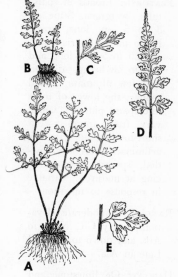

TWO SPLEENWORTS
Mountain: *Plants of:* A. *Average* and B. *Dwarf forms.* C. *Pinna.*
Trudell's: D. *Frond and* E. *Basal pinna.*

CULTURE: Hardly practicable, as with its relatives.

NOMENCLATURE:

Asplenium montanum Willdenow, 1810. (S, FG)

Trudell's Spleenwort, *Asplenium* × *trudelli* Wherry, 1925, resembles the Lobed Spleenwort, but is more symmetrical and deeply cut, with *ca.* 2 pairs of pinnae at base. It occurs rarely at locations where the Lobed and Mountain Spleenworts grow nearby, and is manifestly a hybrid between them. These parents being respectively tetraploid and diploid, it has proved as expected to be triploid.

Wall-rue Spleenwort : *Asplenium ruta-muraria*

FEATURES: Fronds in sparse tufts, evergreen. Stipe *ca.* 3 to 6 cm. long, green. Blade unevenly triangular, *ca.* 2.5 to 5 cm. long and 1.5 to 3 broad, divided into few alternate stalked pinnae, the lower of these into sparse pinnules, which vary from rounded and short-toothed to jaggedly acuminate. Sori few, medial, spaced, but coalescing at maturity. Variable in response to nutrition.

RANGE: At moderate elevations, Surry Co., N.C., to Ark. and down to the Fall Line in Ala.

HABITAT: On limestone and calcareous shale, rooted in firm crevices or in humus among loose rocks, from shady and damp to sunny and dry (then dwarfed); occasionally invading weathered masonry. Soil circumneutral.

WALL-RUE SPLEENWORT
A. *Plant and*   B. *Pinna of type variety. Pinnules of:*   C. *Type and* D. *Narrow variety, enlarged.*

CULTURE: Can be grown in a limestone rock garden, though must be kept from drying out until a new root system develops, which may be aided by removing older fronds when transplanting.

NOMENCLATURE:

Asplenium ruta muraria L., 1753.

AMERICAN REPRESENTATIVE:

A. *ruta muraria* var. *cryptolepis* Wherry, 1942. (FG)
(*A. cryptolepis* Fernald, 1928, basionym.) (S)
A. *ruta muraria* v. *subtenuifolium* Christ, 1903. (FG)
A. *ruta muraria* v. *ohionis* Wherry, 1942, later epithet.
(*A. cryptolepis* v. *ohionis* Fernald, 1928, basionym.) (S)

Cliff Spleenwort : *Asplenium bradleyi*

FEATURES: Fronds few, evergreen. Stipe *ca.* 3 to 6 cm. long, shining dark brown, this coloring extending to middle rachis. Blade *ca.* 6 to 12 cm. long and 1.5 to 3 broad. Pinnae serrate to jagged, with a superior auricle. Sori medial, becoming blackish brown. Originated as a hybrid between Mountain and Brown-stem Spleenworts, with later chromosome-doubling.

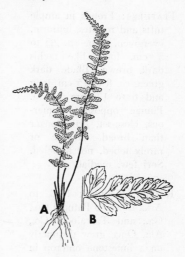

CLIFF SPLEENWORT
A. *Plant.*   B. *Pinna, enlarged.*

RANGE: Piedmont N.C. to Ga. and plateaus of Tenn.–Ala. to Ark.–e. Okla. Discovered in Tenn. in 1870.

HABITAT: Tight crevices in bare, often overhanging cliffs of sandstone, granite, and other lime-free rocks, the humus collecting around its roots strongly acid.

CULTURE: In view of the specialized habitat, this fern, like its relatives, can scarcely be successfully grown.

NOMENCLATURE:

Asplenium bradleyi D. C. Eaton, 1873. (S, FG)

Sand Mountain Spleenwort, *Asplenium* × *gravesii* Maxon, 1918 (FG), was discovered in 1915 west of Trenton, Ga., and has since been found in adj. Ala. Combining the characters of the Cliff and Lobed Spleenworts, it is manifestly their hybrid; as both parents are tetraploid, it, as expected, has proved to have chromosomes of the same ploidy. It has somewhat the aspect of Trudell's Spleenwort, but differs in more rounded divisions and darker stipe, lower rachis, and sori.

Maidenhair Spleenwort : *Asplenium trichomanes*

FEATURES: Fronds in ample tufts and rosettes, uniform, evergreen. Stipe *ca.* 2.5 to 5 cm. long, like rachis dark brown. Blade dark green, *ca.* 8 to 15 cm. long and 6 to 12 mm. broad. Pinnae opposite, numerous, close-set, little longer than broad, crenate or rarely lobed, not auricled. Sori few, medial.

RANGE: Piedmont N.C. to Ark., down to Putnam Co., Ga., and Tuscaloosa Co., Ala. Once grew disjunctly on a limestone outcrop in Winn Par., La.

MAIDENHAIR SPLEENWORT
A. *Plant, reduced.* B. *Pinnae.*

HABITAT: Rock crevices, usually shady and moist, but locally sunny and seemingly dry. Soil circumneutral to moderately acid.

CULTURE: Can be grown in a rock garden, though difficult to establish unless the older fronds are removed when first transplanted.

NOMENCLATURE:

Asplenium trichomanes L., 1753. (S, FG)

A hybrid between the Brown-stem and Maidenhair Spleenworts, known as *Asplenium* × *virginicum* Maxon, 1939, has been collected once in Buncombe Co. in the N.C. mts. It may well occur elsewhere but have been overlooked because it resembles a mere oversized form of the second parent. Its pinnae, however, are distinctly longer and auricled, and the spores are abortive.

Walking Spleenwort : *Asplenium ebenoides*

FEATURES: Fronds exceedingly variable, though always having some features suggesting the Brown-stem Spleenwort (p. 158) and the Walking Fern (next p.), indicating hybridization. The brown color of the stipe extends halfway up the rachis, the blade is usually pinnate only to middle, and the tail-like tip tends to take root. In one Ala. colony the plants reproduce normally, which cytologic study shows to be due to the chromosomes having doubled, resulting in a tetraploid species.

WALKING SPLEENWORT
A. *Plant.*

RANGE: Hybrid plants occur with the parents at a few scattered points from sw. N.C. to nw. Ark., and far n. Ala. The tetraploid colony lies at the Fall Line near Havana, Hale Co., Ala., producing numerous sporelings.

HABITAT: Of the hybrid, limestone and other calcareous rocks, in circumneutral soil. Of the tetraploid, outcrops of conglomerate rock, in both cool-moist and warm-dry ravines, the soil circumneutral to subacid.

CULTURE: The tetraploid is being grown in the north, and should be suitable for southern upland rock gardens.

NOMENCLATURE:

Asplenium [×] *ebenoides* R. R. Scott, 1865.
A. platyneuron × *Camptosorus rhizophyllus* Slosson, 1902.
Asplenosorus ebenoides Wherry, 1937, not validly published.

Walking Fern : *Camptosorus rhizophyllus*

FEATURES: Fronds spreading and arching. Stipe variable in length, brown only at base. Blade simple, thinnish but evergreen, *ca.* 13 to 25 cm. long and 1.5 to 3 broad near base, long-triangular, tapering to an elongate "tail" which often roots at tip. Basal auricles rounded, pointed, or rarely obsolete. Veins areolate. Sori short, scattered in various positions.

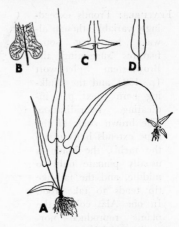

WALKING FERN
A. *Plant, reduced. Blade-bases of:*
B. *Type form.* C. *Long-auricled*
form. D. *Obsolete-auricled form.*

RANGE: Piedmont N.C. to e. Okla., down to n. Ga. and Ala. Locally crossing the Fall Line in ne. Miss.

HABITAT: Best developed on shaded limestone ledges, but occasional on other rocks and even on clay banks. Soil circumneutral or rarely subacid.

CULTURE: Can be grown in a limestone rock garden, most satisfactorily if mulched by limestone-favoring mosses.

NOMENCLATURE:

Camptosorus rhizophyllus Link, 1833. (S, FG)

(*Asplenium rhizophylla* L., 1753; corrected to *rhizophyllum* L., 1763, basionym.) As the genus *Camptosorus* is really only a minor one, a return to the corrected combination of Linnaeus is not unreasonable; herein, however, long-established usage is favored.

The chiefly northern **American Harts-tongue Fern**, *Phyllitis scolopendrium* Newman, 1844 (S), var. *americanum* Fernald, 1935 (FG), once grew disjunctly in large sinks in Tenn.

Woolly Lip Fern : *Cheilanthes tomentosa*

FEATURES: Rootstock thick, bearing copious long narrow scales, sending up tufted fronds which, unlike all our other members of the Common Fern Family, are in bud merely bent instead of coiled. Stipe *ca.* 13 to 25 cm. lg., bearing, like rachis, both scales and hairs. B l a d e bright green, dense-hairy beneath, *ca.* 13 to 25 cm. long and 3 to 6 broad, 3-pinnate; pinnulets round.

WOOLLY LIP FERN
A. *Plant, reduced.*   B. *Pinna.*
C. *Pinnule, enlarged.*

RANGE: Piedmont N.C. to c. Okla., down to the Fall Line in Ga. and Ala.; disjunct in lowlands (p. 200).

HABITAT: Open cliffs and ledges of various rocks, the soil sub-acid to circumneutral.

CULTURE: Attractive and desirable for the rock garden.

NOMENCLATURE:

Cheilanthes tomentosa Link, 1833.

Two related ferns form dense tufts in dryish crevices in limestone in upland Ark. They curl up into whitish clumps during drought, but "resurrect" when moistened:

Slender Lip Fern, *Cheilanthes feei* Moore, 1857. (S, FG). Stipe *ca.* 3 to 6 cm. long. Blade *ca.* 3 to 6 cm. long and 1.5 to 3 broad, densely hairy beneath with white hairs which age buff.

False-cloak Fern, *Notholaena dealbata* Kunze, 1848 (FG). Differing in blade more triangular and laxly divided, and glabrous but covered beneath by white powdery wax.

Hay-scented Fern : *Dennstaedtia punctilobula*

FEATURES: Rootstock wiry, long-creeping, sending up a row of deciduous fronds. Stipe *ca.* 15 to 30 cm. lg., shining red-brown, grading into the yellow-brown rachis, sparse-hairy. Blade yellow-green, *ca.* 23 to 45 cm. long and 13 to 25 brd., 2-pinnate with sharp-lobed pinnules; axes and veins beneath bearing copious glandular hairs exhaling a hay-like scent. Sori globose, borne in a cup-like indusium at tip of a vein, partly covered by a reflexed marginal tooth. Scarcely resembling its lowland relative (p. 226).

RANGE: Piedmont N.C. to mid-Tenn.; disjunct at 2 stations in Ark., and rare down to Fall Line in Ga. and Ala.

HAY-SCENTED FERN
A. *Plant, reduced.*   B. *Pinnule.*
C. *Sorus, enlarged.*

HABITAT: Open or thinly wooded slopes in barren moderately to strongly acid soil; tending to invade pasture-land destructively, since unpalatable to grazing animals. The ability of this seemingly delicate fern to thrive in open sunny situations is remarkable.

CULTURE: Though a beautiful plant, spreads too rapidly for safe admission to a small garden.

NOMENCLATURE:

Dennstaedtia punctilobula Moore, 1857. (S, FG)
(*Nephrodium punctilobulum* Michaux, 1803, basionym.)
Dicksonia punctilobula Gray, 1848, inacceptable genus assignment.

Appalachian Bristle Fern : *Trichomanes radicans,* variety

FEATURES: Rootstock wiry, dark-hairy, creeping over rock-surfaces, producing a row of delicate arching or pendent fronds. Stipe short, winged. Blade only one cell thick, accordingly translucent with color-play, *ca.* 8 to 15 cm. long and 2 to 4 broad toward base, 2-pinnately dissected into pinnule-like segments, their winged axes bearing scattered black hairs. Sporangia borne in soral clusters on long bristles representing vein-extensions into sinuses, surrounded by a short indusioid sheath.

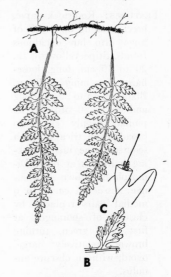

APPALACHIAN BRISTLE FERN
A. *Plant.*   B. *Segment.*
C. *Sorus, enlarged.*

RANGE: Scattered from Polk Co., N.C., to Madison Co., Ark., and northernmost S.C. and Ga.; over Ala. down to Hale Co. on the Fall Line. Reported in Fla.

HABITAT: Shaded moist crevices and cavernous hollows in sandstone and gneiss rocks, often hanging from the roof. Soil decidedly acid.

CULTURE: Might be grown if a habitat resembling its native ones could be constructed.

NOMENCLATURE:

Trichomanes radicans Swartz, 1801, variety. (FG)
Trichomanes boschianum Sturm, 1861. (S)
Vandenboschia radicans Copeland, 1938.

While many workers apply the second-listed epithet to our taxon, none has ever pointed out any significant difference from the widespread one named earlier.

Interrupted Fern : *Osmunda claytoniana*

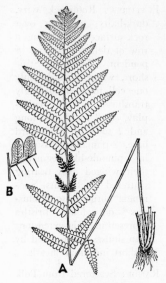

INTERRUPTED FERN
A. *Plant, reduced.*
B. *Sterile segments.*

FEATURES: Rootstock large, erect, sending up a tuft of huge firm but deciduous fronds. Stipe yellowish, *ca.* 20 to 40 cm. long, loose-hairy, becoming glabrous. Blade *ca.* 45 to 90 cm. long and 15 to 30 brd. Sterile pinnae deeply cut into broad symmetrical obtusish segments, the rachis lacking hair-tufts at base. Dimorphism shown by pinnae: tissue in *ca.* 2 to 6 medial pairs replaced by clusters of sporangia, at first dark green, turning brown, relatively large, ovoid, with an obscure annulus.

RANGE: Scattered, north-Piedmont N.C. to Ark. and down to Forsyth Co., in Piedmont Ga. Seemingly nowhere close to the Fall Line.

HABITAT: Wooded slopes and hummocks in swamps, only exceptionally mingling with other members of the genus. Soil subacid to circumneutral, relatively rich in mineral nutrients.

CULTURE: Readily grown and desirable in a cool-climate woodland garden.

NOMENCLATURE:
Osmunda claytoniana L., 1753. (S, FG)

The colloquial name of this fern refers to the curious way in which the fertile pinnae interrupt the regular rows of sterile ones.

Lace-Leaf Grape Fern : *Botrychium dissectum*

FEATURES: Plant appearing in summer. Stipe *ca.* 3 to 6 cm. and blade-stalk 5 to 10 long. Blade evergreen, bronzing in winter and withering in spring, broad-triangular, *ca.* 4 to 8 cm. long and 6 to 12 broad, 3-pinnate below to 1-pinnate toward tip. Margins jaggedly cut into coarse teeth which are not serrate, but have entire sub-parallel sides and a truncate tip.

RANGE: Scattered, Piedmont N.C. to nw. Ark., down to Cobb Co., Ga.; not approaching lowlands.

HABITAT: Damp woods and thickets. Soil low in mineral nutrients and moderately acid.

LACE-LEAF GRAPE FERN
A. *Plant, reduced.*
B. *Bit of margin, enlarged.*

CULTURE: Not known to have been successfully grown in the southern uplands.

NOMENCLATURE:

Botrychium dissectum Sprengel, 1804. (S, FG) (Also termed "var. *dissectum*" or "type var.")

   SHALLOWLY-CUT FORM:

B. *dissectum* f. *confusum* Bartholomew, 1951.
(*B. obliquum* f. *confusum* Wherry, 1942, basionym.)

In the north the SHALLOWLY-CUT FORM is so frequent that *B. obliquum* gets made a variety of *B. dissectum*. In the south, however, both *B. dissectum* and this form are so rare that it is simpler to recognize two distinct species.

Field Horsetail : *Equisetum arvense*

FEATURES: Rootstock much-branched, with roots and tubers at nodes. Stem many-ridged, traversed by canals, the central one *ca.* ⅓ the over-all diameter, bearing at nodes crown-like sheaths with scarious teeth representing leaves. Dimorphism extreme: Fertile stems arising in early spring, *ca.* 15 to 30 cm. high, succulent and soon withering, pinkish, the flaring sheaths with blackish-brown teeth. Spores green, globose, with ribbon-like appendages, borne in ovoid sporangia in a cone.

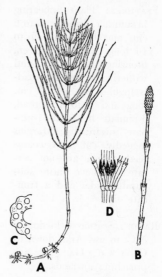

FIELD HORSETAIL
A. *Plant with sterile shoot and*
B. *Fertile shoot, both reduced.*
C. *Half section, enlarged.*
D. *Node, enlarged.*

Sterile stems appearing as the fertile fade, green, *ca.* 25 to 50 cm. high, or in forms developing in disturbed ground spreading to prostrate. Sheathed nodes bearing whorls of green branches resembling slender stems.

RANGE: Rare and scattered, along n. border of our region from lowland N.C. to nw. Ark., down to Fulton Co., Ga., and far n. Ala.

HABITAT: Damp woods, swamps, stream banks, and meadows, invading road and railroad fills and other barren disturbed ground. Soil subacid to circumneutral.

CULTURE: Too weedy for admission to the garden.

NOMENCLATURE:

Equisetum arvense L., 1753. (S, FG)

Rock Spike-moss : *Selaginella rupestris*

FEATURES: Aspect moss-like, but tissues traversed by long tubular cells as well as strengthening fibers. Plants forming evergreen mats, *ca.* 2.5 to 5 cm. high. L e a v e s narrow, crowded in multiple spiral rows, up to *ca.* 2 mm. long and 0.5 mm. broad, ciliate, tipped by a firm white bristle. Cone square-prismatic, *ca.* 1 to 2 cm. lg.

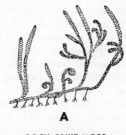

A

ROCK SPIKE-MOSS
A. *Plant*

Sporophyls ovate. Sporangia globose, a few containing 2 or 4 relatively large yellowish female megaspores but most of them numerous minute reddish male microspores.

RANGE: Piedmont N.C. to e. Okla., down nearly to the Fall Line in N.C., S.C., Ga., and Ala.

HABITAT: In full sun or rarely part shade, on sheets of gravelly humus over sandstone, granite, and similar hard rocks, in our region seemingly not invading sandy ground. Soil mostly subacid.

CULTURE: Can be transplanted to a lime-free rock garden if kept moist until established.

NOMENCLATURE:

Selaginella rupestris Spring, 1838. (S, FG)
(*Lycopodium rupestre* L., 1753, basionym.)

This Spike-moss can be distinguished from those treated on page 280 by its occurrence only in the uplands, where its long stems, supported by the rhizophores characterizing the genus, spread into springy mats.

Crowfoot Clubmoss : *Lycopodium flabelliforme*

FEATURES: Stem long-creeping in thin litter, its evergreen branches *ca.* 15 to 30 cm. high, branched in a fan-like pattern, to which the epithet refers. Branchlets formed into flat strips *ca.* 2 mm. broad by the fused bases of 4 rows of close-set leaves: the top row narrow, appressed, the side ones broad, spreading, and the bottom with only its tiny tail-like tip free. Annual constrictions rare. Peduncle *ca.* 5 to 10 cm. long, often 2-forked and bearing 4 cones *ca.* 2.5 to 5 cm. lg.

RANGE: Piedmont N.C. to mid-Tenn. and rare southward down to Fulton Co. in the Ga. Piedmont.

CROWFOOT CLUBMOSS
A. *Plant, reduced.*
B. *Under side of branchlet.*
C. *Sporophyl, enlarged.*

HABITAT: Dry or rarely moist open woods, thickets, and grassy slopes, in mostly subacid humus-rich soil.

CULTURE: Desirable as a ground-cover in a cool-climate acid-soil woodland garden, but when transplanted must be kept from drying out until new roots develop.

NOMENCLATURE:

Lycopodium flabelliforme Blanchard, 1911. (S, FG)
(*L. complanatum* v. *flabelliforme* Fernald, 1901, basionym.)

In the southern uplands no form of this Clubmoss really resembles the far northern Flat-branch species, so to use the name of the latter, *L. complanatum*, without adding the varietal epithet (as is sometimes done) leads to geographic confusion.

Ground-cedar : *Lycopodium tristachyum*

FEATURES: Rootstock creeping well below the soil surface. Erect shoots evergreen, *ca.* 15 to 30 cm. high, in the open bluish green and funnel-shaped with numerous close-set branches, in the shade bright green with these spaced, sprawly. Branchlets formed into strips *ca.* 1.5 mm. broad by the fused bases of 4 rows of close-set leaves, the top row narrow and appressed, the side ones broadish and spreading, and the bottom with a subulate tip nearly as long as adjacent side ones. Annual constrictions well-developed and conspicuous. Peduncle *ca.* 4.5 to 9 cm. long, often 2-forked and bearing 4 short-stalked slender cones *ca.* 1.5 to 3 cm. long.

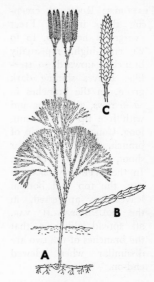

GROUND-CEDAR
A. Plant, reduced. B. Under side of branchlet. C. Cone.

RANGE: A northern (and European) species, extending rarely into the mountains of N.C. and adj. Tenn.

HABITAT: Rocky barrens and open coniferous woods. Soil low in nutrients and strongly acid.

CULTURE: Not known to have been grown successfully in gardens in our region.

NOMENCLATURE:

Lycopodium tristachyum Pursh, 1814. (S, FG)

L. chamaecyparissus A. Braun, 1843; applied in Europe without realization that the same species had previously been named in America.

Ground-pine : *Lycopodium obscurum*

FEATURES: Rootstock creeping deep in soil. Erect evergreen shoots *ca.* 13 to 25 cm. high, repeatedly branched upward, so tree-like. Leaves shining dark green, on the branches in *ca.* 6 rows, all narrow and with free tip 3 to 5 mm. long. Cone sessile at tip of branch, *ca.* 1 to 10 per shoot, *ca.* 3 to 5 cm. lg. In the TYPE FLAT-BRANCH VAR. the top and bottom leaves are appressed, in the ROUND-BRANCH VAR. all spread alike, so that the branches of the two are dissimilar when viewed end-on.

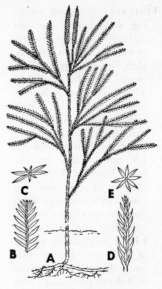

GROUND-PINE
A. *Plant, reduced.   Branchlet-tips of Flat-branch (type) variety:*
B. *Under side.   C. End view.*
D. *and E., same of Round-branch variety, all enlarged.*

RANGE: Inner Piedmont and mts. of N.C., down to nw. S.C. and ne. Ala.; both vars. are present, but the flat-branch one is more frequent.

HABITAT: FLAT-BRANCH VAR., moist to dry humus-rich woods, the soil mostly subacid and well-supplied with nutrients; ROUND-BRANCH VAR., acid mossy barrens.

CULTURE: Desirable for a cool-climate acid-soil woodland garden.

NOMENCLATURE:

TYPE, FLAT-BRANCH VAR.:
Lycopodium obscurum L., 1753. (S, FG)
ROUND-BRANCH VAR.:
Lycopodium obscurum v. *dendroideum* D. C. Eaton, 1890. (FG)
(*L. dendroideum* Michaux, 1803, basionym.)

Running Clubmoss : Lycopodium clavatum

FEATURES: Stem creeping through litter, sending up evergreen forking branches *ca.* 13 to 25 cm. high. Leaves light green, ascending, in *ca.* 10 spiraled rows, narrowly linear, *ca.* 3.5 to 7 mm. long with bristle up to 3 mm. long at tip, all alike so that the branch-outline is round. Tip of branchlets sending up a peduncle *ca.* 8 to 15 cm. long, forked near tip and bearing few slender cones *ca.* 4 to 8 cm. long.

RANGE: Mts. of N.C. and adj. Tenn.

HABITAT: Open woods, grassy thickets, and rocky barrens, in subacid humus-rich soil.

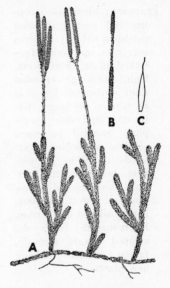

RUNNING CLUBMOSS
A. *Plant, reduced.*
B. *Stem-tip of One-cone variety.*
C. *Leaf, enlarged.*

CULTURE: Worthy of trial in a cool-climate acid-soil woodland garden; the plants must be kept moist after transplanting until new roots form.

NOMENCLATURE:

Lycopodium clavatum L., 1753. (S, FG)

Stiff Clubmoss, *Lycopodium annotinum* L., 1753 (FG) ranges down the Va. mts. and may enter our region: there is actually a specimen preserved which is alleged to have been collected in Tenn. many years ago, although the species has never been rediscovered there. It differs from the above in having stiff dark-green spreading leaves and solitary cones sessile at branch-tip.

Shining Clubmoss : *Lycopodium lucidulum*

FEATURES: Stem-base creeping and rooting, holding persistent old leaves. Stems evergreen, up-curving, few-forked, to *ca.* 13 to 25 cm. high, bearing crowded shiny dark-green leaves in *ca.* 6 rows, the longer sterile ones and short sporophyls grouped in zones, yielding a knobby effect; sterile *ca.* 6 to 12 mm. long, broadened and serrate above middle, sporophyls *ca.* 4 to 8 mm. long, less broadened and serrate. Heart-shaped buds, developed toward stem-tip, falling off and yielding new plants.

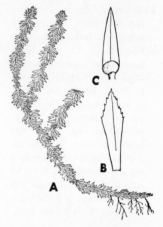

SHINING CLUBMOSS
A. *Plant, reduced.* B. *Leaf and*
C. *Sporophyl, enlarged.*

RANGE: Piedmont N.C. to mid-Tenn., down to Rabun Co., in Ga. mts.

HABITAT: Wooded slopes, flats, and stream banks, the soil rich in humus and usually subacid.

CULTURE: Readily transplanted and desirable for a cool-climate woodland garden, the shining dark-green knobby stems producing a striking effect.

NOMENCLATURE:

Lycopodium lucidulum Michaux, 1803. (S, FG)
Urostachys lucidulus Herter, 1909.

This and the two following taxa represent the most primitive division of the genus, in that their sporophyls are borne in zones on leafy stems instead of on differentiated cones. It is on this basis that they are sometimes assigned to an independent genus.

Rock Clubmoss : *Lycopodium porophilum*

FEATURES: Stem-base short-creeping and rooting, with some persistent old leaves. Stems evergreen, forking at base and somewhat upward, curving up or down and yielding tufts and festoons, *ca.* 8 to 15 cm. long. Leaves bright green though scarcely shiny, the sterile ones *ca.* 4.5 to 9 cm. and sporophyls 3.5 to 7 mm. long, in zones pro-

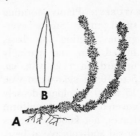

ROCK CLUBMOSS
A. *Plant, reduced.*
B. *Leaf, enlarged.*

ducing a moderately knobby effect, flat, narrowed above middle, at most obscurely serrate. Locally seeming to grade into both the preceding and following.

RANGE: Widely scattered in mts. of N.C. and S.C., out to mid.-Tenn. and down to Winston Co., Ala.

HABITAT: Crevices in cliffs, ledges, and rock-slides, the soil sub-acid to circumneutral.

NOMENCLATURE:

Lycopodium porophilum Lloyd & Underwood, 1900. (S, FG)
Urostachys lucidulus v. *porophyllus* Herter, 1909, misprint.
Lycopodium lucidulum v. *occidentale* L. R. Wilson, 1932.
(*L. lucidulum* f. *occidentale* Clute, 1903, basionym.)
(*L. selago* v. *patens* Desvaux, 1827, sometimes mistakenly applied to the present taxon.)

Unfortunately the chromosomes in this group of Clubmosses are unusually minute and numerous, so that it has not yet proved practicable to account for the seeming intergradation between the three members.

Mountain Clubmoss : *Lycopodium selago*

FEATURES: Plants forming small tufts. Stems evergreen, rooting at base, forked there and sparingly upward, in TYPE VAR. *ca.* 5 to 10, in SPREADING VAR. 15 to 30 cm. long, densely covered with uniform leaves, not knobby. Leaves broad and concave at base, tapering upward, entire or barely serrate, in TYPE VAR. *ca.* 4 to 8 and SPREADING VAR. 5 to 10 mm. long; sporophyls like sterile leaves, so that their zones are not manifest. Heart-shaped buds which can grow into new plants often abundant.

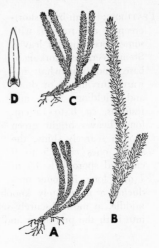

MOUNTAIN CLUBMOSS
Plants of varieties: A. Appressed-leaf. B. Spreading-leaf. C. Type. D. Leaf, enlarged.

RANGE: This species being chiefly arctic and northern, its occurrence in our region seems rather anomalous, yet it is actually not uncommon on north-facing cliffs in the higher mts. of N.C. and S.C., down to Rabun Co., Ga. Reports of it from lower elevations are based on misidentified plants of the Rock Clubmoss.

HABITAT: In moist mossy humus on cool or bleak chiefly north-facing cliffs of sandstone, granite, and gneiss. Soil strongly acid. Culture deemed impracticable.

NOMENCLATURE:

TYPE VARIETY:

Lycopodium selago L., 1753. (S, FG)

Urostachys selago Herter, 1909.

SPREADING VARIETY:

Lycopodium selago var. *patens* Desvaux, 1827. (FG)

(*Plananthus* (*Lycopodium*) *patens* Palisot de Beauvois, 1805, basionym.)

INDEXES

AUTHORS OF FERN NAMES

Adanson, Michel, 1727–1806; French taxonomist (1 taxon)
Agardh, Jakob G., 1813–1901; Swedish taxonomist (1)
Aiton, William, 1731–1793; British taxonomist (1)
Alston, Arthur H. G., 1902–1958; British pteridologist (2)
Ascherson, Paul F. A., 1834–1913; German taxonomist (1)
Aublet, J. B. C. F., 1720–1778; French taxonomist (1)

Baker, John G., 1834–1920; British pteridologist (5)
Beddome, Richard H., 1830–1911; British pteridologist (1)
Benedict, Ralph C., 1883–   ; American pteridologist (1)
Bernhardi, Johann J., 1774–1850; German taxonomist (5)
Blake, Sidney F., 1892–1959; American taxonomist (1)
Blasdell, Robert F., 1929–   ; American taxonomist (1)
Blume, Karl L. von, 1796–1862; Dutch taxonomist (1)
Bonpland, Aimé J. A., 1773–1858; French taxonomist (3)
Bory de St. Vincent, Jean . . . , 1778–1846; Fr. naturalist (2)
Braun, Alexander C. H., 1805–1877; German taxonomist (9)
Brongniart, Adolphe T., 1801–1876; French taxonomist (1)
Broun, Maurice, 1906–   ; American naturalist (2)
Brown, Clair A., 1903–   ; American botanist (1)
Brown, Robert, 1773–1858; British taxonomist (1)
Burman, Johannes, 1706–1779; Dutch taxonomist (3)
Butters, Frederick K., 1878–1945; American taxonomist (1)

Cavanilles, Antonio J., 1745–1804; Spanish taxonomist (3)
Chapman, Alvan W., 1809–1899; American taxonomist (5)
Ching, Ren-Chang, 1899–   ; Chinese pteridologist (1)
Christensen, Carl F. A., 1872–1942; Danish pteridologist (15)
Clausen, Robert T., 1911–   ; American taxonomist (1)
Clute, Willard N., 1869–1950; American pteridologist (3)
Copeland, Edwin B., 1873–1964; American pteridologist (7)
Correll, Donovan S., 1908–   ; American taxonomist (3)
Curtiss, Allen H., 1845–1907; American naturalist (1)

Desvaux, A. Niçaise, 1784–1856; French taxonomist (4)
Diddell, Mrs. W. D.,   –   ; American horticulturist (1)

Diels, Friedrich L. E., 1874–1945; German taxonomist (1)
Domin, Karel, 1882–1954; Czechoslovakian botanist (1)
Durieu de Maisonneuve, Michel C., 1797–1878; French pteridologist (1)

Eaton, Alvah A., 1865–1908; American pteridologist (3)
Eaton, Amos, 1776–1842; American taxonomist (1)
Eaton, Daniel C., 1834–1895; American pteridologist (3)
Engelmann, George, 1809–1884; American taxonomist (3)

Farwell, Oliver A., 1867–1944; American taxonomist (4)
Featherman, Americus, 1822–   ; American naturalist (1)
Fée, Antoine L. A., 1789–1874; French pteridologist (11)
Fernald, Merritt L., 1873–1950; American taxonomist (6)
Fischer, Friedrich E. L., 1782–1854; Russian taxonomist (3)
Forskål, Pehr, 1732–1763, Swedish taxonomist (1)

Galeotti, Henri G., 1814–1858; Belgian taxonomist (2)
Gaudichaud-Beaupré, Charles, 1789–1854; Fr. taxonomist (1)
Gay, Jacques E., 1786–1864; Swiss taxonomist (1)
Gilbert, Benjamin D., 1835–1907; American pteridologist (2)
Gmelin, Johann F., 1709–1755; German taxonomist (1)
Gray, Asa, 1810–1888; American taxonomist (4)
Greville, Robert K., 1794–1866; British taxonomist (1)
Grisebach, August H. R., 1814–1879; German taxonomist (1)

Harper, Roland M., 1878–   ; American taxonomist (1)
Hawkes, Alexander D.,   –   ; Amer. horticulturist (1)
Heller, A. Arthur, 1867–1944; American taxonomist (2)
Herter, Wilhelm G., 1884–1958; German–South American taxonomist (1)
Heward, Robert, 1791–1877; British taxonomist (1)
Hieronymus, Georg H. E. W., 1846–1921; German taxon. (5)
Holden, Isaac, 1832–1903; American naturalist (1)
Hooker, (Sir) William J., 1785–1865; British taxonomist (6)
Humboldt, Friedrich H. A. von, 1769–1859; German nat. (3)

Jacquin, Nikolaus J. von, 1727–1817; Austrian taxonomist (3)
Jenman, George S., 1845–1902; British taxonomist (1)
Johnston, Ivan M., 1898–1960; American taxonomist (1)

Koidzumi, Gen'ichi, 1883–   ; Japanese taxonomist (1)
Kuhn, Maximilian F. A., 1842–1894; German taxonomist (2)
Kuntze, C. E. Otto, 1843–1907; German taxonomist (6)
Kunze, Gustav, 1793–1851; German pteridologist (10)
Kurata, Satoru, 1922–   ; Japanese pteridologist (1)

Lamarck, J. B. . . . de, 1744–1829; French naturalist (2)
Langsdorf, Georg H. von, 1774–1852; German botanist (3)
Lawson, George, 1827–1895; Canadian naturalist (1)
Link, Johann H. F., 1767–1851; German taxonomist (10)
L. = Linnaeus, Carolus (Carl von Linné), 1707–1778; Swedish
    taxonomist (67). "L., Jr.," 1741–1783 (2)
Lloyd, Francis E., 1868–1947; Canadian botanist (2)

Martens, Martin, 1797–1863; Belgian taxonomist (2)
Masamune, Genkai, 1899–   ; Japanese botanist (1)
Maxon, William R., 1877–1948; American pteridologist (9)
Mettenius, Georg H., 1823–1866; German taxonomist (3)
Michaux, André, 1746–1802; French–American taxonomist (6)
Moore, Thomas, 1821–1887; British pteridologist (6)
Morton, Conrad V., 1905–   ; American pteridologist (3)
Moxley, George L., 1871–   ; American naturalist (1)
Muhlenberg, G. Henry E., 1753–1815; Amer. taxonomist (1)
Munz, Philip A., 1892–   ; American taxonomist (1)

Newman, Edward, 1801–1876; British pteridologist (1)
Nieuwland, Julius A. A., 1878–1936; American taxonomist (1)
Nishida, Toji, 1874–1927; Japanese taxonomist (1)

Oakes, William, 1799–1848; American taxonomist (1)

Palisot de Beauvois, Ambroise M. F. J., 1752–1820; French
    pteridologist (4)
Palmer, William, 1856–1921; American naturalist (1)
Pfeiffer, Norma E., 1889–   ; American botanist (1)
Poeppig, Eduard F., 1798–1868; German taxonomist (1)
Poiret, Jean L. M., 1755–1834; French taxonomist (3)
Prantl, Karl A. E., 1849–1893; German taxonomist (3)
Presl, Karel B., 1794–1852; Austrian pteridologist (30)
Proctor, George R., 1920–   ; American pteridologist (2)

Rafinesque, Constantine S., 1783–1840; naturalist (1)
Retzius, Anders J., 1742–1821; Swedish taxonomist (1)
Richard, Louis C. M., 1754–1821; French taxonomist (1)
Roth, Albrecht W., 1757–1834; German pteridologist (2)

Sadebeck, Richard E. B., 1839–1905; German pteridologist (1)
St. John, Edward P., 1866–1952; American pteridologist (13)
St. John, Robert P., 1869–1960; American pteridologist (9)
Savigny, M. J. C. L., 1777–1867; French naturalist (1)
Schkuhr, Christian, 1741–1811; German taxonomist (3)
Schmidel, Casimir C., 1718–1792; German taxonomist (1)
Schott, Heinrich W., 1794–1865; Austrian pteridologist (7)
Schrader, Heinrich A., 1767–1836; German taxonomist (1)
Schreber, Johann C. D., 1739–1810; German taxonomist (1)
Scopoli, Giovanni A., 1723–1788; Italian naturalist (1)
Small, John K., 1869–1938; American taxonomist (18)
Smith, (Sir) James E., 1759–1828; British taxonomist (9)
Smith, John, 1798–1888; British horticulturist (7)
Sodiro, Luis, 1836–1909; Spanish botanist (1)
Sprengel, Kurt P. J., 1766–1833; German taxonomist (3)
Spring, Anton F., 1814–1872; Belgian taxonomist (2)
Swartz, Olof P., 1760–1818; Swedish taxonomist (28)

Tardieu-Blot, Mme. Marie L., 1902–   ; French pteridol. (1)
Thunberg, Carl P., 1743–1828; Swedish taxonomist (2)
Tidestrom, Ivar, 1864–1956; American taxonomist (2)
Torrey, John, 1796–1873; American taxonomist (1)
Tryon, Rolla M., 1916–   ; American pteridologist (3)
Tuckerman, Edward, 1817–1886; American naturalist (1)

Underwood, Lucien M., 1853–1907; Amer. pteridologist (19)

Van Eseltine, Glen P., 1888–1938; American taxonomist (1)

Wagner, Warren H., Jr., 1920–   ; American naturalist (3)
Wallich, Nathaniel, 1786–1854; British pteridologist (1)
Walter, Thomas, 1740–1789; American taxonomist (1)
Watt, David A. P., 1830–1917; Canadian pteridologist (1)
Weatherby, Charles A., 1875–1949; Amer. pteridologist (4)
Wherry, Edgar T., 1885–   ; American naturalist (8)
Willdenow, Karl L., 1765–1812; German taxonomist (6)

EPITHETS AND THEIR SIGNIFICANCE

abscissum: cut off, 170
acanthonota: with a row of spines, 280
acrostichoides: resembling an *Acrostichum,* 134
adiantifolia: with leaves like an *Adiantum,* 236
adiantoides: resembling an *Adiantum,* 226
adiantum-nigrum: a black *Adiantum,* 168
adpressum: turned toward a support, 284
alabamense (-is): of Alabama, 96, 198, 258
alata: winged, 270
albolineata: white-lined, 208
alopecuroides: resembling an *Alopecurus* (Foxtail), 288
americana: of America, 264
amesiana: in honor of Oakes Ames, 136
ampla (-um): ample, 140
angustifolia (-um): narrow-leaved, 66
anthriscifolium: with leaves like *Anthriscus* (Chervil), 168
apiifolia: with leaves like *Apium* (Celery), 130
apoda (-um): without a foot, 274
appressum: pressed against a support, 284
apus: without a foot, 274
aquilina (-um): like an eagle, 220
arenicola: growing in sand, 280
areolata (-um): having areoles, 148
armata: armored, 276
asplenioides: resembling an *Asplenium,* 126
atropurpurea: dark purple, 202
augescens: increasing, 110
aurea (-um): golden, 74, 184
auritum: having ear-like appendages, 170
australis: southern, 144

bacculum-rubrum: of Baton Rouge, 160
bahamensis: of the Bahamas, 206
bigelovii: in honor of Jacob Bigelow, 284
bipinnata: twice-pinnate, 226
biscayneanum: of Biscayne Bay, 176

biserrata (-um): doubly serrate, 214
biternata (-um): doubly ternate, 260
brasiliense: of Brazil, 72
braunii: in honor of Alexander Braun, 278

calomelaena (-anos, -as): showy black, 182
capillus-veneris: hair of Venus, 190
caroliniana (-um): of Carolina, 266, 284
caudata (-um), 218
celsa: held high, 146
cernua (-um): nodding, 282
chapmani: in honor of A. W. Chapman, 270, 288
cicutaria: resembling *Cicuta* (Water-hemlock), 138
cinnamomea: like cinnamon, 242
clavata (-um): club-shaped, 224
conformis: shapely, 94
cordifolia (-um): with heart-shaped leaves, 216
coriandrifolia (-um): with leaves like Coriander, 138
costatum: ribbed, 66
cretica: of Crete, 208
cristata (-um): crested, 144, 172
crotalophoroides: bearing rattles like a snake, 252
cuneatum: wedge-shaped, 192
curtissii: in honor of A. H. Curtiss, 174

danaeaefolium: with leaves like *Danaea,* 180
deltoidea: shaped like the Greek letter delta, 186
dendroneuron: with branched nerves, 250
dentata (-us, -um): toothed, 98
dichotomum (-us): forked, 290
dissectum: dissected, 262
diversifolia: with varied leaves, 206

eatoni: in honor of A. A. Eaton, 276
ebeneum: like ebony, 158
elatum: tall, 268
elongatum: elongate, 288
engelmanni: in honor of George Engelmann, 248, 272
ensiformis: sword-shaped, 208
esculenta (-um): edible, 122
exaltata (-um): especially tall, 216

excelsum: lofty, 180
exiguum: scant, 70

falcata (-um): scythe-shaped, 132
ferrissi: in honor of J. H. Ferriss, 268
filifolia: with thread-like leaves, 188
filix-femina: female fern, 126
flaccida: limp, 270
flexuosa: bending back and forth, 228
floridana (-um): of Florida, 142, 252
fragilis: brittle, 82

germani: in honor of M. —— Germain, 234
gongylodes (goggilodus): with rounded projections, 96
grandifolia: large-leaved, 212

haleana: in honor of Josiah Hale, 102
harperi: in honor of R. M. Harper, 114
heracleifolia (-um): with leaves like Hercules' drug, 138
heterochroum: varying in color, 164
heterophylla (-um): with varying leaves, 70
hexagonoptera (-um): with hexagonal wings, 84
hiemale: variant spelling of hyemale, 268
hispidulum: minutely bristly, 196
hyemale (Linnaeus' spelling): of winter, 268

incisum: sharply cut, 160, 166
indicum: of India, 154
inundatum: covered by water, 288

japonicum: of Japan, 124, 238

krausii: in honor of Dr. Kraus, collector, 232
kraussiana: in honor of Herr —— Krauss, 278
kunzeana: in honor of Gustav Kunze, 178

lanceolata (-um): conventionally lance-shaped, 76
lanosa (-um): woolly, 200
latiuscula (-um): broadish, 220
latum: broad, 68
lindheimeri: in honor of F. J. Lindheimer, 112
lineata: marked with lines, 188

patens: spreading, 108
pectinata (-um): comb-like, 62, 214
petersii: in honor of Thomas M. Peters, 232
petiolatum: with a stalk at base of blade, 252
phyllitidis: resembling a *Phyllitis,* 68
phymatodes: bearing warts, 64
pilosa: hairy, 86
pinetorum: of pines, 206
pinnatum: feather-like in pattern, 286
platyneuron (-os): broad-veined, 158
plenum: full, 172
plumula: like a small feather, 64
polypodioides: resembling a *Polypodium,* 60
prealtum (praealtum): very tall, 268
prostratum: lying flat, 286
protrusa (-um): protruding, 82, 190
pseudocaudata (-um): imitating taxon *caudatum,* 220
pseudopodum: with a false foot, 254
pteridoides: resembling a *Pteris,* 186
pubescens: soft-hairy, 102
pumilum: rather small, 168
punctatum: marked with dots, 232
punctilobula: with small pointed lobes, 226
pycnocarpon (-us): with crowded fruits, 128
pycnostichum: with crowded rows (of sporangia), 254

quadrangulare (-is): four-angled, 100

radicans: taking root, 94
reducta: reduced in size (downward), 98
regalis: royal, 244
repens: creeping, 222
reptans: crawling, 94
resiliens: springy, 164
resinifera (-um): bearing resin or wax, 106
reticulatum: netted, 88
rhizophyllum: with rooting leaves, 174
riddellii: in honor of J. L. Riddell, 280
robustum: stout, 268

saxatilis: occurring among rocks, 118
scalifolium: scaly-leaved, 174

scolopendria (-um) : like a segmented worm, 64
sensibilis: sensitive, 78
serra: like a saw, 110
serratum: saw-toothed, 88, 166
serrulatum: finely saw-toothed, 154
setigera: bristle-bearing, 104
sherwoodii: in honor of W. L. Sherwood, 278
spectabilis: showy, 244
sphenoides: wedge-shaped, 232
submarginale (-is) : within the margin, 140
subtetragona (-um) : not quite four-sided, 92
subtile: delicate, 172
swartzii: in honor of Olof Swartz, 70

tenerum: tender, 250
tenuifolia (-um) : slender-leaved, 178
tetragona (-um) : four-angled, 92
thelypterioides: resembling a *Thelypteris,* 120
thelypteris: a female fern, 102
torresiana (-um) : in honor of D. L. de Torres, 104
tortipila: with twisted hairs, 278
trifoliata (-um) : three-leaved, 184
tripartita: divided into three parts, 212
triquetrum: three-cornered, 292
triseriale: in three rows, 72
tunbridgense: occurring at Tunbridge Wells, 230

uliginosa (-um) : of swamps, 104
unca: bent at tip, 114
uncinata: hooked, 264
unitum: joined, 96

verecundum: modest, 174
versicolor: varying in color, 120
victoriae: honoring Queen Victoria, 208
virginiana (-um) : of Virginia, 256; virginica (-um), 150
viridis: green, 202
vittata: striped, 204
vulgaris, vulgatum: common, 64, 254

willdenovii: in honor of C. L. Willdenow, 278

TECHNICAL NAMES

ACCEPTED GENERA

COMBINATIONS

(Accepted ones in bold-face type)

NEW COMBINATIONS

Seven name-combinations believed to be made for the first time in this *Guide* are herewith validated by citing the place of original publication of the epithet:

(70) *Microgramma heterophylla* (L.) Wherry, *comb. nov.*
Polypodium heterophyllum L., *Sp. Pl.,* p. 1083, 1753.

(72) *Goniophlebium triseriale* (Swartz) Wherry, *comb. nov.*
Polypodium triseriale Swartz, *Journ. Bot., Schrader,*
1800[2]: 26, 1801.

(86) *Leptogramma pilosa var. alabamensis* (Crawford) Wherry,
comb. nov.
Thelypteris pilosa var. *alabamensis* Crawford, *Amer.*
Fern Journ. 41: 16, 1951.

(90) *Goniopteris sclerophylla* (Kunze) Wherry, *comb. nov.*
Aspidium sclerophyllum Kunze, *Syst. Veg., Sprengel,*
4: 98, 1827.

(110) *Thelypteris* × *lindheimeri* (Christensen) Wherry, *stat. nov.*
Thelypteris normalis var. *lindheimeri* Christensen,
Danske Vid. Selsk. Skr. VII.10: 182, 1913.

(114) *Thelypteris normalis var. harperi* (Christensen) Wherry,
comb. nov.
Dryopteris normalis var. *harperi* Christensen, *Danske*
Vid. Selsk. Skr. VII.10: 182, 1913.

(168) *Asplenium pumilum var. anthriscifolium* (Jacquin) Wherry,
stat. nov.
Asplenium anthriscifolium Jacquin, *Collectanea* 2:103,
pl. 2, 1788.

These combinations are also to be published in periodical literature.

COLLOQUIAL NAMES